Grade **6**

Scott Foresman

Fresh Reads
for Fluency and Comprehension
Teacher's Manual

Glenview, Illinois

Boston, Massachusetts

Chandler, Arizona

Upper Saddle River, New Jersey

PEARSON

The Pearson Promise

As the largest educational publishing company in the world, Pearson is committed to providing you with curriculum that not only meets the Common Core State Standards, but also supports your implementation of these standards with your students.

Pearson has aligned the Common Core State Standards to every grade level of *Scott Foresman Reading Street*, our premier educational curriculum. This product provides an alignment of the Common Core State Standards to the Grade 6 assessment items in *Scott Foresman Reading Street Fresh Reads for Fluency and Comprehension*.

We value your partnership highly and look forward to continuing our mission to provide educational materials that fully satisfy your classroom needs.

ISBN 13: 978-0-328-72640-0
ISBN 10:   0-328-72640-0
4 5 6 7 8 9 10 V036 21 20 19 18 17 16 15 14 13

Contents

Unit 4 Explorers, Pioneers, and Discoverers

Unit 5 Resources

Unit 6 Exploring Cultures

NOTES TO THE TEACHER

Introduction

Fresh Reads for Fluency and Comprehension is designed to provide differentiated practice in reading comprehension skills and to prepare students to take the Reading/Language Arts section of standardized tests, state tests, or teacher-made tests. The student book includes the weekly differentiated practice tests to strengthen comprehension skills taught in *Scott Foresman Reading Street.* This Teacher's Manual includes the following: (1) notes on how to use the Fresh Read tests, (2) instructions on how to administer and score a fluency test, (3) two charts on which you may record the progress of your students, and (4) annotated copies of all of the Fresh Read tests indicating the correct answer to all questions.

How to Use the Fresh Read Tests

The purpose of the Fresh Read tests is to give weekly differentiated practice in target comprehension skills taught in *Scott Foresman Reading Street.*

This book contains three Fresh Read tests for each week to be used independently from the main selection in *Scott Foresman Reading Street.* The tests consist of a "Fresh Read" leveled passage and related comprehension items that focus on the target and review comprehension skills of the week but are written to address varying levels of proficiency—Strategic Intervention (SI), On-Level (OL), and Advanced (A). A code at the bottom of each page tells you the level of each test.

You can assess student's proficiency levels using their responses to discussion questions in class and their work on the comprehension pages in the Reader's and Writer's Notebook. Fresh Read tests can be done independently, or you may choose to work through them with students in small groups, in order to give support and assess student's progress.

Other ways to use the Fresh Read test pages:

- use the Strategic Intervention pages for whole-class practice with the comprehension skills and/or test-taking skills

- use the Strategic Intervention pages after introducing the target and review comprehension skills but prior to reading the main selection in the student anthology of *Scott Foresman Reading Street* to assess students' readiness to read that selection

- use the On-Level pages as an assessment tool to check students' understanding of the comprehension skills and/or test-taking skills

- use the On-Level pages to check students' need for further practice, reteaching, or more challenging materials

- use the Advanced pages as a substitute for the comprehension pages in the Reader's and Writer's Notebook for students working above grade level

- use any of the pages as preparation for the Unit Benchmark Test

How to Administer and Score a Fluency Test

A fluency test measures a student's reading rate, or the number of words correctly read per minute (wcpm), on grade-level text the student has not seen before. You may want to use a copy of one of the "On-Level" leveled passages from the Fresh Read tests for this purpose. Make a photocopy for yourself of the passage you will give the student. (The pages in this Teacher's Manual have a scale of running numbers to make it easier for you to know how many words the student read during the fluency check, while the passages in the student edition do not have the numbers.) Make sure you have put the student's name and the test date at the top of your copy of the passage. Have a watch or clock with a second hand available for timing the reading.

Give the student a copy of the passage for the test. Note: The student should NOT have seen the passage beforehand; it is a "fresh" reading passage for the student. Do NOT allow the student to read the passage silently before oral reading.

Have the student read the text aloud. Do not have the student read the title as part of the fluency reading; it is not included in the running word count. (You may want to tape-record the student's reading for later evaluation.) Stop the student at exactly one minute and note precisely where the student stopped.

As the student reads orally, on your copy of the text mark any miscues or errors the student makes during the reading (see the chart on page viii). Count the total number of words the student read in one minute. Subtract any words the student read incorrectly. Record the words correct per minute score on the test.

The formula is: Total # of words read – # of errors = words correct per minute (wcpm).

You will likely want to keep the test in your folder for the child. You may also want to record children's progress on the Reading Fluency Progress Chart on page xi and/or the Individual Fluency Progress Chart, Grade 6 on page xii.

How to Identify Reading Miscues/Errors

Using the passage on page ix, the chart below shows the kinds of miscues and errors to look for as a student reads aloud and the notations to use to mark them.

Reading Miscue	Notations
Omission The student omits words or word parts.	Anjelo (had) visited his cousin in Connecticut the summer before.
Substitution The student substitutes words or parts of words for the words in the text.	As they approached Sells, Michael could see ~~the~~ *a* beautiful green dome on the Pima County courthouse.
Insertion The student inserts words or parts of words that are not in the text.	Sells wasn't as big or as hot as Michael *had* expected. ^
Mispronunciation/Misreading The student pronounces or reads a word incorrectly.	Anjelo knew what Michael *accepted* expected when he came to Arizona.
Hesitation The student hesitates over a word and the teacher provides the word.	So on the ride from the Tuscon airport toward Sells, the capital of the Tohoro O'odham Nation near the Mexican border, Michael gaped at the huge saguaro cacti they passed.
Self-correction The student reads a word incorrectly but then corrects the error.	"It's not the biggest Indian (SC) reservation in Arizona."

Notes

- If the student hesitates over a word, wait several seconds before telling the student what the word is.

- If a student makes the same error more than once, count it as only one error.

- Self-correction is not counted as an actual error. However, writing "SC" over the word or words will help you identify words that give the student some difficulty.

Sample Fluency Test

Here is the passage marked as shown on the previous page. This is the "On-Level" passage from Grade 6, Unit 1, Week 1. As the student reads the passage aloud to you, mark miscues and errors. Have the student read for exactly one minute, and then mark the last word the student reads.

Old Yeller

Name _Susan_   9/4/2009   (122)

Anjelo's Nation

accepted	
Anjelo knew what Michael expected when he came to Arizona. Anjelo (had)	12
visited his cousin in Connecticut the summer before, and Michael kept insisting that	25
Arizona was all a flat, dry desert. So on the ride from the Tucson airport toward	41
Sells, the capital of the Tohoro O'odham Nation near the Mexican border, Michael	54
gaped at the huge saguaro cacti they passed.	62
"Nation," Michael had mumbled the first time he heard the name. "It must really	76
be a small one."	80
"It's not the biggest Indian reservation in Arizona," Anjelo agreed, noting that it	93
was, however, about the size of Connecticut.	100
As they approached Sells, Michael could see the beautiful green dome on the	113
Pima County courthouse. Sells wasn't as big or as hot as Michael expected. Anjelo	127
explained that they were more than two thousand feet above sea level and that it	142
seldom got hotter than eighty degrees there in the summer. Still, Michael couldn't	155
resist suggesting that they stop and buy some bottled water just in case they ran out.	171

127 - 5 = 122

Total number of words read	**127**
Number of errors	**– 5**
Words correct per minute	**122**

Interpreting the Results

According to published norms for oral reading fluency, students at the end of Grade 6 should be reading fluently at 150 words correct per minute in text that is on grade level. This chart gives recommended progress toward that goal.

End of Unit/Grade		Reading Rate (wcpm)
Grade 6	Unit 1	115 to 120
Grade 6	Unit 2	120 to 126
Grade 6	Unit 3	125 to 132
Grade 6	Unit 4	130 to 138
Grade 6	Unit 5	135 to 144
Grade 6	Unit 6	140 to 150
End of Year Goal		150

If a student's reading rate is lower than the suggested progress toward the standard for his or her grade level, your notes on the student's miscues may help you determine why the rate is low. Does the student make errors that indicate his or her decoding skills are poor? If so, further instruction in phonics may be needed. Do the errors reflect a lack of comprehension or limited vocabulary? In that case, instruction in comprehension strategies and exposure to more vocabulary words may help. A lack of fluency may indicate a lack of exposure to models of fluent oral reading. It may also mean that the student isn't reading enough material at his or her reading level. Encourage the student to read more books or magazine articles at an accessible or comfortable level of reading for him or her.

Reading Fluency Progress Chart

Student's Name	Unit 1		Unit 2		Unit 3		Unit 4		Unit 5		Unit 6	
	Date	WCPM	Date	WCPM	Date	WCPM	Date	WCPM	Date	WCPM	Date	WCPM
1.												
2.												
3.												
4.												
5.												
6.												
7.												
8.												
9.												
10.												
11.												
12.												
13.												
14.												
15.												
16.												
17.												
18.												
19.												
20.												
21.												
22.												
23.												
24.												
25.												
26.												
27.												
28.												
29.												
30.												
31.												
32.												
33.												
34.												
35.												

Individual Fluency Progress Chart, Grade 6

Name _____

WCPM values (vertical axis): 180, 175, 170, 165, 160, 155, 150, 145, 140, 135, 130, 125, 120, 115, 110, 105, 100, 95, 90, 85

Timed Reading/Week (horizontal axis): 1, 2, 3, 4, 5, 6, 7, 8, 9, 10, 11, 12, 13, 14, 15, 16, 17, 18, 19, 20, 21, 22, 23, 24, 25, 26, 27, 28, 29, 30

WCPM

Timed Reading/Week

Fresh Reads for Fluency and Comprehension

Name _____

Read the selection. Then answer the questions that follow.

Grandma's Dollhouse

Brandi asked Sandra to accompany her on a visit to Grandma Thisler's house.	13
"She's a wonderful little lady," Brandi said. "I'm just not comfortable in her house."	27
They walked through a fancy wooden gate and up a winding narrow path. "Her	41
house looks like a miniature cottage in a fairy tale!" Sandra whispered.	53
Inside, the girls sat in very small chairs covered with doilies. Plants in tiny pots	68
covered little tables. Brandi seemed nervous and sat with her shoulders up almost	81
around her ears, but Sandra was delighted.	88
Grandma Thisler served hot chocolate, and they chatted about the relatives in tiny	101
pictures all around the small room.	107
Later, when the girls got up to depart, a doily stuck to Sandra's arm. She turned to	124
pick it off, and her elbow knocked a plant off a table.	136
"Whew!" Sandra said outside.	140
"I thought you loved the place," Brandi teased.	148
"I felt like a clumsy doll!" Sandra said.	156

Turn the page.

Answer the questions below.

1 Which of the following statements best describes Grandma Thisler's place?

   A It is filled with magical things.

   B It is large and fancy like a palace.

   (C) It is small and crowded inside.

   D It is ugly and nearly empty.

2 What did Sandra think of Grandma Thisler's house when she first arrived there?

   (F) She loved it and thought it was wonderful.

   G She was uncomfortable and worried.

   H She could not believe it was real.

   J She wished she could live there.

3 What probably changed Sandra's feeling about Grandma Thisler's house?

   A Grandma Thisler served bitter tasting hot chocolate.

   B Grandma Thisler wanted them not to stay long.

   C Sandra saw how uncomfortable Brandi was there.

   (D) Sandra accidentally knocked a plant off of a little table.

4 Explain what characteristics of Grandma Thisler's house made Sandra feel like "a clumsy doll."

Possible response: Grandma Thisler's house is small like a dollhouse and full of frames, plants, and things you might break if you aren't very careful. Sandra felt like a doll in a dollhouse.

Common Core State Standards

Questions 1–3: Literature 5. Analyze how a particular sentence, chapter, scene, or stanza fits into the overall structure of a text and contributes to the development of the theme, setting, or plot. **Question 4: Literature 1.** Cite textual evidence to support analysis of what the text says explicitly as well as inferences drawn from the text.

Read the selection. Then answer the questions that follow.

Anjelo's Nation

Anjelo knew what Michael expected when he came to Arizona. Anjelo had visited	13
his cousin in Connecticut the summer before, and Michael kept insisting that Arizona	26
was all a flat, dry desert. So on the ride from the Tucson airport toward Sells, the	43
capital of the Tohono O'odham Nation near the Mexican border, Michael gaped at the	57
huge saguaro cacti they passed.	62
"Nation," Michael had mumbled the first time he heard the name. "It must really be	77
a small one."	80
"It's not the biggest Indian reservation in Arizona," Anjelo agreed, noting that it was,	94
however, about the size of Connecticut.	100
As they approached Sells, Michael could see the beautiful green dome on the Pima	114
County courthouse. Sells wasn't as big or as hot as Michael expected. Anjelo explained	128
that they were more than two thousand feet above sea level and that it seldom got hotter	145
than eighty degrees there in the summer. Still, Michael couldn't resist suggesting that	158
they stop and buy some bottled water just in case they ran out.	171
"No shortage of water here," Anjelo said, laughing. "It rains a lot in the summer, and	187
our deep wells fill up. Travelers stop here just to taste the delicious water."	201
Anjelo outlined the agenda for the weeks Michael was to be there. They would go	216
to the desert museum, its zoo, and the botanical garden in Tucson. Another day they	231
would see more than 250 historic planes in the air and space museum there. Anjelo	246
anticipated that the best time would be the camping trip they would take high into the	262
nearby mountains, where there were waterfalls splashing in the crisp, refreshing air.	274
Michael's vacation would be full of surprises.	281

Turn the page.

- -

Answer the questions below.

1 Anjelo's cousin Michael thinks that Arizona is

    A bigger than Connecticut.

    (B) nothing but desert.

    C very mountainous.

    D cold in the summer.

2 From the brief description in this story, which of these would be the best way to describe the area where Anjelo lives in Arizona?

    (F) a varied landscape

    G high in the mountains

    H wet, lush, and green

    J a barren landscape

3 What can Michael expect on his vacation?

    A He will be stuck in a small town far from nowhere.

    (B) He will see and do many interesting things.

    C There will be little to do to pass the time.

    D The heat will make him very uncomfortable.

4 What is the water situation in Sells?

    F People have to survive on bottled water.

    G The place is often flooded.

    (H) They have all the good drinking water they need.

    J Their water is pumped in from Tucson.

5 Why was Michael surprised?

Arizona was not as hot and dry as he had expected.

_____

_____

_____

_____

Common Core State Standards

Questions 1–4: Literature 5. Analyze how a particular sentence, chapter, scene, or stanza fits into the overall structure of a text and contributes to the development of the theme, setting, or plot. **Question 5: Literature 1.** Cite textual evidence to support analysis of what the text says explicitly as well as inferences drawn from the text.

Name _____

Read the selection. Then answer the questions that follow.

They Still Can Fly

Great Uncle Fred saw in the newspaper that airplanes like those he had flown in World	16
War II would be at the airport, and he wanted someone to go with him to see them.	34
"Big jets, huh?" I said.	39
"We didn't have jets in those days, Andy," Uncle Fred said, laughing. "These are a	54
B17 and a B24."	58
Our airport has one paved runway and a small cement block terminal. Otherwise,	71
it looks a lot like an empty, unplanted field. Uncle Fred followed other cars around a	87
fence to park on the grass.	93
We saw the planes on display to one side of the runway, and I was amazed at how	111
small they were. They weren't sleek and modern, the way I expected war airplanes to	126
be. They looked boxy, awkward, and kind of ugly.	135
People crowded around them, staring up at names of their crews painted on their	149
sides. We peered into the small glass turrets on their bellies and tails, where men	164
squeezed in beside machine guns. We climbed a rickety metal ladder into the barrel of	179
each plane and walked very carefully from the tail to the cockpit, squeezing past empty	194
bays where bombs were carried.	199
The tight interiors of the planes were bare metal pieces bolted together, with	212
openings in the sides and floors. I wondered how cold and frightening it must have	227
been for the crew and tried to imagine Uncle Fred as a young pilot.	241
We were very quiet coming back to town. We stopped at a grocery, and when we	257
came out, a strange vibrating noise filled the sky. Flying overhead was the rickety old	272
B17 that I had been lucky enough to see up close.	283

Turn the page.

Answer the questions below.

1 Most of this story takes place
   A outside of a grocery store.
   B inside an airport terminal.
   C in a new jet airplane.
   (D) around and in old airplanes.

2 Which is the best phrase to describe the airport?
   F sleek and modern
   G boxy and awkward
   (H) empty and unused
   J cold and frightening

3 What did Andy notice most about the planes' insides?
   (A) They seemed small and crowded.
   B They looked very modern.
   C There were names written on them.
   D They were very long and roomy.

4 What did seeing the planes make Andy think about?

Andy thought about what it was like for Uncle Fred as a pilot.

5 The next day Andy told a friend that the crew of a B17 must have been really brave men. What did he most likely say about the B17 to help his friend understand?

Flying in the sky in such a cramped and small airplane must have been frightening.

Common Core State Standards

Questions 1–3: Literature 5. Analyze how a particular sentence, chapter, scene, or stanza fits into the overall structure of a text and contributes to the development of the theme, setting, or plot. **Questions 4, 5: Literature 1.** Cite textual evidence to support analysis of what the text says explicitly as well as inferences drawn from the text.

Name _____

Read the selection. Then answer the questions that follow.

For the Fun of It

The neighborhood children played soccer that summer on an empty, grassy field.	12
The competition began by choosing up teams, and Matthew hated that. He was fast, but	27
his big feet wouldn't change directions easily. Matthew never anticipated being chosen	39
first, but Katie always picked him early in the selection process. She was a terrific	54
soccer player and scored lots of goals.	61
"How come you always choose me?" Matthew asked her. "My big clown feet won't	75
help us win."	78
"Because it's fun to have you on our team," Katie said.	89
The players used huge cardboard boxes for their goals. One day Matthew's dad drove	103
up with goals made of plastic pipe and big netting. Everyone thanked him joyfully.	117
"It was Matthew's idea," Matthew's father said. "He figured out how we could	130
make them."	132
Katie looked at Matthew with a proud smile.	140

Turn the page.

Answer the questions below.

1 Why did Matthew dislike choosing sides for soccer teams?

A He knew that Katie would expect him to win the game.

B He thought choosing teams was a waste of time.

(C) He felt as if he was not good enough to be chosen early.

D He did not believe Katie really wanted him on her team.

2 What is most likely Katie's main reason for playing soccer?

(F) to have fun with her friends

G to show off her soccer talent

H to have Matthew on her team

J to help Matthew learn to play better

3 Which is the *best* summary of this story's plot?

A A father makes soccer goals that his son's soccer team can use.

B Children in a neighborhood have to play soccer in an empty field.

(C) A boy finds a way to help his soccer team even though he isn't a great player.

D A girl's teammates think a boy is a poor soccer player, but she still picks him.

4 What can you learn from Katie's actions in the story?

Possible response: You should never judge people just on their sports abilities, because they may have other good things to offer.

Common Core State Standards

Questions 1, 2, 4: Literature 3. Describe how a particular story's or drama's plot unfolds in a series of episodes as well as how the characters respond or change as the plot moves toward a resolution. Question 3: Literature 2. Determine a theme or central idea of a text and how it is conveyed through particular details; provide a summary of the text distinct from personal opinions or judgments.

Name _____

Read the selection. Then answer the questions that follow.

The Backpack Litter

Arthur, the librarian, didn't deliberately acquire cats. He couldn't say no to a	13
homeless critter and had ended up with eleven feline roommates. Even strangers	25
seemed to know about Arthur's affinity for cats.	33
One spring day, a college girl plunked her backpack on Arthur's desk and slowly	47
reached in it to lift out a sleepy white kitten. She kept dipping into her bag, and	64
eventually she was shuffling four frisky kittens to keep them all on top of Arthur's desk.	80
None seemed any the worse for the ride in the backpack.	91
The student explained that the kittens had been born four weeks before and needed a	106
home. Arthur's mouth formed the words, "Oh, no!"	114
"I'm leaving town," the young woman said. "I can take their mother home with me,	129
but not the litter. If you won't rescue them, they're destined to go to the shelter."	145
Arthur's cat family was very upset about the newcomers, so he called Maggie, a	159
friend who had lost a cat after twenty years. He insisted that she come and adopt just	176
one kitten.	178
Reluctantly, Maggie picked up an orange kitten. When she turned to leave with it, a	193
black and white one was perching on her foot, clinging to her pants leg. "OK," she said,	210
"I'll adopt these two."	214
When she got to the door, Maggie looked back at the round black kitten and the tiny	231
white one, sadly watching their remaining family depart. They seemed to be saying,	244
"Wait, what's going on here?"	249
"All right!" Maggie said, sighing and grimacing at Arthur. "I'll take all four and keep	264
them together."	266

Turn the page.

Answer the questions below.

1 Which of the following best describes how Arthur feels about cats?

A needy

B suspicious

(C) protective

D uninformed

2 Which of these is a theme of the story?

F Bad decisions are generally made in great haste.

G Having pet animals can ease loneliness for people.

(H) Good deeds can mean taking on more than expected.

J Choices made based on feelings turn out to be unwise.

3 Which event is the climax of the story?

A A student brings four kittens in for the librarian.

B Arthur saves four kittens from going to the shelter.

C Arthur's cat family dislikes the four new kittens.

(D) Maggie comes to take one kitten but takes all four.

4 When the student told Arthur that the kittens would go to the shelter if he didn't take them, she was most likely

(F) trying to persuade him to take them.

G suggesting that the shelter might be a better place for kittens.

H hoping to impress Arthur with his ability to take care of cats.

J thinking that would scare the kittens into behaving.

5 Compare Maggie and Arthur. Are they alike or different? Tell how.

They are alike in that they both love cats and feel sorry for them when they need a home. They are different in that Arthur has eleven cats while Maggie, who once had only one cat, now has four.

Common Core State Standards

Questions 1, 2, 5: **Literature 3.** Describe how a particular story's or drama's plot unfolds in a series of episodes as well as how the characters respond or change as the plot moves toward a resolution. Questions 3, 4: **Literature 2.** Determine a theme or central idea of a text and how it is conveyed through particular details; provide a summary of the text distinct from personal opinions or judgments.

Read the selection. Then answer the questions that follow.

Who's Critical Now?

"Davie needs to calm down considerably," Felix announced at lunch, as if it were an	15
absolute fact. "He's a real comedian, but sometimes he embarrasses me by being too	29
silly and upsetting adults."	33
"Juanita has lots of relatives in Mexico," he went on. "But we'd never know that	48
because she doesn't seem to know anything about Mexico." Juanita shrugged in	60
agreement when he added, "She didn't even know about Cinco de Mayo. I had to tell	76
her what it was and why lots of people celebrate it."	87
An Yang and Felix were close friends, but she didn't escape his judgment. "An Yang	102
is way too positive in the way that she never criticizes her friends. She ought to let us	120
know what she likes about us and recommend ways we could improve."	132
An Yang responded immediately to Felix's suggestion that she should let her friends	145
know what was wrong with them. "The trouble with you, Felix," she said, "is that no	161
one ever has to guess what you think. You can't talk about people—or anything for that	178
matter—without revealing exactly what you think."	185
"He's too mouthy, is what he is," Davie contributed. "He has interesting comments	198
about people and other stuff, but I get really tired of it eventually."	211
"Well, his continual judgment hurts my feelings sometimes," Juanita said, "and	222
anyway, he's not always perfectly right about everything."	230
"Ahem!" Felix grunted, looking at his friends with a serious face. "I was going	244
to admit that you guys are not as opinionated as I am, but you just made that really	262
difficult."	263

Turn the page.

Answer the questions below.

1 Which character appears most sensitive to criticism?

  A Davie

  (B) Juanita

  C An Yang

  D Felix

2 This story takes place

  F at the city park.

  G in the library.

  H at Felix's house.

  (J) in the lunchroom.

3 Which of the following best describes Felix?

  A protective

  B unconcerned

  C cautious

  (D) talkative

4 Describe each character's reactions to Felix's criticisms.

An Yang responds by telling Felix that everyone knows he speaks his mind. Davie says that he gets tired of Felix's talking. Juanita admits that she's hurt by the criticisms.

5 What lesson does Felix learn from his friends' reactions to his criticism?

Possible response: If you are critical of your friends, they may one day be equally critical of you.

Common Core State Standards

Questions 1, 3–5: Literature 3. Describe how a particular story's or drama's plot unfolds in a series of episodes as well as how the characters respond or change as the plot moves toward a resolution. **Question 2: Literature 1.** Cite textual evidence to support analysis of what the text says explicitly as well as inferences drawn from the text.

Read the selection. Then answer the questions that follow.

First Things First

They called themselves "The Young Yanks," and they were on their way home from	14
Yankee Stadium after a baseball game in the last month of the season.	27
On the subway, Tao decided to play a game to pass the time. "If you had your choice	45
between a weeklong vacation in a rustic cabin in the Pocono Mountains and one on the	61
beach at Atlantic City, which would you pick?"	69
"That's easy," Keith said. "I'd pick the mountains, even if it just meant living out in a	86
tent. I'd want good fishing and some canoeing too."	95
Tao groaned.	97
"Oh, man," Shing said, "I'd love to stroll the boardwalk in Atlantic City for a week,	113
and relax in the sun and splash around in the water."	124
They all looked at Claudio, waiting for his choice. "I'd stay right here, guys," he	139
said, giving Tao a thumbs up. "The baseball playoffs are coming up soon for the	154
pennant. My team needs me right here."	161

Turn the page.

Answer the questions below.

1 Which of the boys would most likely be considered an outdoorsman?
- **(A)** Keith
- **B** Shing
- **C** Claudio
- **D** Tao

2 Which boy appears to dislike camping out?
- **F** Keith
- **G** Shing
- **H** Claudio
- **(J)** Tao

3 What activity probably appeals most to Shing?
- **A** camping in a tent
- **B** fishing in the ocean
- **(C)** going swimming
- **D** watching baseball

4 How do you know that Claudio is a serious baseball fan?

He won't even consider a vacation while baseball is still being played.

Common Core State Standards

Questions 1–4: Literature 1. Cite textual evidence to support analysis of what the text says explicitly as well as inferences drawn from the text.
Literature 3. Describe how a particular story's or drama's plot unfolds in a series of episodes as well as how the characters respond or change as the plot moves toward a resolution.

Read the selection. Then answer the questions that follow.

An Important Decision

When the Martinez family moved to the big city, Yoli had a very important decision | 15

to make. She would have the choice of attending Jefferson Public School (Number 27) | 29

or Kendleton Middle School. | 33

Jefferson was an old structure in a suburb just across a river that ran through | 48

downtown, and it served the area where Yoli's family lived. Jefferson had long halls | 62

that echoed the voices of its students, but it was built of warm brown brick, and Yoli | 79

thought it had a friendly-looking entrance. | 85

Kendleton was both old and new. It was part of a plan the city had initiated within | 102

its school system to buy unusual buildings and turn them into newly designed schools. | 116

There was a high school on a couple of floors of a big office building, for example, | 133

and Kendleton had been created in an abandoned factory. It was near downtown, and | 147

everything in it was new and very sleek and modern. | 157

Yoli visited both schools and had lunch in their cafeterias. The students and teachers | 171

at both schools seemed very friendly. At Kendleton, there was an attractive gymnasium | 184

that also served as an auditorium, but at Jefferson, the principal, Mrs. Abbingez, asked | 198

Yoli a lot of questions about Yoli's life and family. She took the time to find out what | 216

kinds of activities interested Yoli. | 221

When it came time to choose, Yoli's parents expected her to select Kendleton | 234

because it was so new and interesting, but Yoli kept thinking about Mrs. Abbingez and | 249

picked Jefferson. | 251

Turn the page.

Answer the questions below.

1 Compared to Kendleton, Jefferson Middle School was

   A boldly modern in structure.

   (B) an old-fashioned brick school.

   C designed as an office building.

   D old and in need of many repairs.

2 What part of her new school's building helped Yoli make up her mind?

   F its halls

   G the cafeteria

   H the gymnasium

   (J) its entrance

3 What does Jefferson have that Kendleton may not have?

   A friendly students

   B a cafeteria

   (C) an interested principal

   D a high school very nearby

4 What does Yoli's decision tell us about her?

   (F) People are more important to her than buildings.

   G Modern buildings are not attractive to her.

   H She likes to visit new and different places.

   J She does not like noise or crowds.

5 How are the Kendleton and Jefferson school buildings alike?

Jefferson is an old building, and Kendleton is built in an old factory building.

Common Core State Standards

Questions 1–5: Literature 1. Cite textual evidence to support analysis of what the text says explicitly as well as inferences drawn from the text.

Read the selection. Then answer the questions that follow.

Playing the Game

The sixth graders at Eastview Middle School played *Scrabble*® when Mrs. Martin	12
introduced the game in class. They used wooden tiles with letters on them to form	27
words. They placed the tiles on the game boards she had brought.	39
They consulted dictionaries to find words to make with some of the seven letters	53
each player had drawn, and classmates who observed were encouraged to assist the	66
players. Edmundo and Christa maintained a list on the chalkboard of all the words	80
being created.	82
After the initial play, an additional word had to connect to some word already on the	98
board. Tony liked to keep the board "open" with lots of places for interesting words to	114
cross or touch other words. He often played his words near pink and blue squares that	130
doubled or tripled the points of letters or whole words. Tony hoped his opponents could	145
play on those and earn big scores too.	153
Chuck tried to place letters on those colored squares himself, being careful not to	167
create opportunities for other players. His objective was to score more points than his	181
opponents. He even reread the rules and announced that using dictionaries was not	194
allowed.	195
Chuck discovered that clever *Scrabble* players can bluff by creating words that aren't	208
really words. Would the made-up word *stigits,* for example, lead his opponents to	221
challenge it or to worry about losing a turn if it really was a word?	236
Mrs. Martin praised Tony's approach, but Chuck was the one who got his classmates	250
to learn the actual rules and to compete during the activity period. By the next year,	266
members of the Eastview *Scrabble* Team were competing in tournaments. Chuck won	278
one and his picture appeared in the local newspaper.	287
Scrabble is a registered trademark of Hasbro, Incorporated.	295

Turn the page.

Answer the questions below.

1 Who wanted to play the game the way it is meant to be played?

   A Mrs. Martin

   B Tony

   C Christa

   (D) Chuck

2 Who was probably responsible for starting the Eastview Scrabble Team?

   F Tony

   G Christa

   (H) Chuck

   J a newspaper reporter

3 Compared to Tony's approach, Chuck's approach to playing the game made Chuck

   A less likely to win.

   B more considerate of other players.

   C less interested in words.

   (D) more competitive.

4 What excited Tony most about playing Scrabble?

Possible response: Tony would get excited about seeing the words everyone would form.

5 Why was Tony's approach to Scrabble probably more pleasing to Mrs. Martin than Chuck's approach was?

Possible responses: Tony's approach makes learning new words while having fun more important than winning. Chuck's way makes winning the most important thing.

Common Core State Standards

Questions 1–3: Literature 3. Describe how a particular story's or drama's plot unfolds in a series of episodes as well as how the characters respond or change as the plot moves toward a resolution. **Questions 4, 5: Literature 1.** Cite textual evidence to support analysis of what the text says explicitly as well as inferences drawn from the text.

Name _____

Read the selection. Then answer the questions that follow.

It Can Be Nice to Dream

The Nutcracker ballet is a beloved holiday tradition. In it, young Clara dreams that	14
her toys come alive. A nutcracker shaped like a soldier, a gift from her godfather, leads	30
toy soldiers into battle. Clara has to save the nutcracker from the evil mouse king and	46
his army.	48
Soon the nutcracker becomes a prince. He and Clara dance with snowflakes in the	62
Land of Snow. Then they meet the sugar plum fairy in the Land of Sweets.	77
Very creative productions of this ballet have been designed around the world for	90
more than one hundred years. At our Bijou Theater last night, a huge screen (really	105
a frame), was hung at the rear of the stage. In the frame behind her, Clara's dreams	122
came to life while she stood dreaming in front of it. Gradually, the characters from	137
her dreams appeared onstage to wake her to dance and, near the end of the scene, a	154
sleeping Clara (played by another actress) was alone in the frame.	165
This clever staging showed how our dreams can live beside our realities. It was nice	180
to be reminded!	183

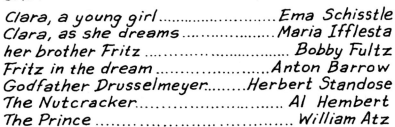

The Bijou Theater Ballet
December 18
The Nutcracker
Music by Pyotr Ilyich Tchaikovsky
Based on a book by E.T.A. Hoffman

CAST

Clara, a young girl .... Ema Schisstle
Clara, as she dreams .... Maria Ifflesta
her brother Fritz .... Bobby Fultz
Fritz in the dream .... Anton Barrow
Godfather Drusselmeyer......... Herbert Standose
The Nutcracker........................... Al Hembert
The Prince .... William Atz

Turn the page.

Answer the questions below.

1 Based on the selection, which of the following is a statement of opinion?
(A) The big frame hung at the back of the stage was a good idea.
B *The Nutcracker* ballet has been staged all over the world.
C *The Nutcracker* ballet is based on elements of Clara's dreams.
D Modern versions of old ballets can include creative staging.

2 Which of the following, based on the selection, is a statement of fact?
F Clara's godfather meant for his gift to inspire her to dream.
(G) In her dream, Clara defeats the evil mouse king.
H The author is an expert on and lover of traditional ballets.
J *The Nutcracker* ballet focuses on confusion between fantasy and reality.

3 The music for this ballet was written by
(A) Tchaikovsky.
B Hoffman.
C Schisstle.
D Bijou.

4 There were two actresses playing Clara onstage at the same time. What does this staging suggest?

Possible responses: It shows how our dreams and realities can exist simultaneously. It can also show how our dreams can become our realities.

Common Core State Standards

Questions 1, 2: Informational Text 8. Trace and evaluate the argument and specific claims in a text, distinguishing claims that are supported by reasons and evidence from claims that are not. **Questions 3, 4: Informational Text 1.** Cite textual evidence to support analysis of what the text says explicitly as well as inferences drawn from the text.

Name _____

Read the selection. Then answer the questions that follow.

The Awesome Backpack

Margaret Kay was shopping for a new backpack when she saw an advertisement for	14
the *Rock-It!* "Wow!" she cried out loud. "That is the coolest backpack I've ever seen!"	29
The *Rock-It!* was long and sleek, with a big flap at the top that opened to a full-	47
length, deep pocket and had a zipper covered by a waterproof fly seal that kept books	62
and papers dry from any rain or snow. Another flap halfway down opened to a hard-	78
case storage pocket, which was actually a lightweight plastic box sewn in to protect	91
more valuable possessions.	94
Stored under that were C batteries that ran two blue lights flashing out of the bottom	110
of the backpack, to look like jets—they were purely for decoration. Between the	124
student and the backpack, there was an attached inflatable comfort pad to cushion the	138
student's back.	140
"What are the lights for?" Margaret Kay's mother asked.	149
"Aren't they the most awesome thing you've ever seen?" Margaret Kay said.	161
"The air-filled pad is sensible," her mother responded, "but there's no pocket for	174
pencils. This just doesn't seem to be a wise purchase. Let's browse at the mall for one	191
with wheels so you can roll it on the pavement when your back gets tired."	206

The *Rock-It!* Backpack

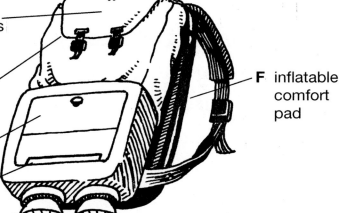

A full-length, deep pocket for books

B waterproof "fly" seal

C hard-case storage pocket

D storage for batteries

E *Rock-It!* lights

F inflatable comfort pad

Turn the page.

Answer the questions below.

1 Which of the following represents a statement of opinion?

   A Margaret Kay saw an advertisement for the *Rock-It!*

   B The backpack had a zipper covered by a waterproof fly seal.

   (C) The *Rock-It!* was better than other backpacks.

   D Two blue lights were purely for decoration.

2 The batteries that run the lights of the *Rock-It!* were stored

   F under the top flap.

   G in the hard-case pocket.

   H under the inflatable comfort pad.

   (J) near the bottom of the backpack.

3 Based on the story, which of the following is a statement of fact?

   A The *Rock-It!* sold very well.

   B Margaret Kay got a backpack with wheels.

   C The *Rock-It!* plastic case for valuables cracked easily.

   (D) Margaret Kay and her mother disagreed about backpacks.

4 Based on information in the story, what is Margaret Kay's mother's opinion of the blue lights?

   F They are a fire hazard.

   (G) They are interesting but useless.

   H Rain might ruin them.

   J After dark, they will work as reflectors.

5 Which feature of the *Rock-It!* backpack is most likely to be different for different wearers?

Possible responses: The inflatable comfort pad could help someone who has sore muscles or an injury. The inflatable comfort pad may not be comfortable for everyone.

Common Core State Standards

Questions 1, 3, 4: Informational Text 8. Trace and evaluate the argument and specific claims in a text, distinguishing claims that are supported by reasons and evidence from claims that are not. **Questions 2, 5: Informational Text 1.** Cite textual evidence to support analysis of what the text says explicitly as well as inferences drawn from the text.

Name _____

Read the selection. Then answer the questions that follow.

Dragging Canoe's Losing Battle

For more than sixty years, the Cherokee suffered from the smallpox epidemic and	13
from battles with tribes that tried to claim their land in the Carolinas. The Cherokee	28
have been called warlike because they often fought the French and eventually turned	41
against their uneasy ally, the British. They felt that a good offense was essential to keep	57
their land, which stretched west to the Mississippi River. In fact, Cherokee villages	70
suffered raids by white settlers.	75
In 1750, twelve-year-old Tsi'ui-Gunsin'ni wanted to join the battle, but no one	87
believed he was old enough and strong enough to fight. He was challenged to pull a	103
fully loaded log canoe from the shore into the water. He performed the task and earned	119
the name Dragging Canoe. Dragging Canoe suspected that the Cherokee people would	131
ultimately lose most of their land to the American settlers, so he spent the rest of his	148
life refusing to yield to them or the French.	157
In 1775, Richard Henderson, a businessman from North Carolina, bought twenty	168
million acres of land from the Cherokee for a mere two thousand pounds of sterling and	184
six wagon loads of goods. Dragging Canoe insisted that Henderson was swindling the	197
Cherokee out of their ancestral hunting grounds.	204
Although the Henderson deal was made invalid by both the British and American	217
governments, Dragging Canoe fought on, choosing to side with the British in the	230
Revolutionary War, not the American settlers. In one battle, he was severely wounded	243
though he made a recovery. After a final victory, it was said that he celebrated too	259
much, for he died the next morning at the age of fifty-four.	271
The Americans won the Revolutionary War against the British, and by 1838 almost	284
all of the Cherokee land had been taken over by the settlers—just as Dragging Canoe	300
had predicted.	302

Dragging Canoe was once the leader of Malaqua, a Cherokee town on an island in the Little Tennessee River. It is now completely flooded by the Tellico Dam.

Turn the page.

Answer the questions below.

1 Based on the selection, which of the following is a statement of opinion?

A The Cherokee have been called warlike.

(B) Henderson cheated the Cherokee out of their lands.

C Dragging Canoe never gave up fighting to keep Cherokee land.

D Dragging Canoe was one of the youngest Indian braves to go to battle.

2 Based on information in the selection, which of the following is a statement of fact?

F The Cherokee would have fared better had they not sided with the British.

(G) The Cherokee fought aggressively to keep their land.

H Henderson hoped to obtain Indian land for an unfairly low price.

J The land Henderson bought was taken over by the British.

3 Which of the following statements supports the opinion that Tsi'ui-Gunsin'ni would make a good warrior?

(A) Tsi'ui-Gunsin'ni was confident in his abilities to fight in battle.

B Tsi'ui-Gunsin'ni always dreamed of becoming a warrior.

C Tsi'ui-Gunsin'ni was not strong enough to fight.

D Tsi'ui-Gunsin'ni was twelve years old.

4 What does the caption of the picture tell you about Dragging Canoe as a grown man?

He became a leader of one town his people lived in.

5 What does the Tellico Dam's location suggest about Dragging Canoe's prediction about the future?

Dragging Canoe accurately predicted that the Cherokee would lose their land.

Common Core State Standards

Questions 1–3: Informational Text 8. Trace and evaluate the argument and specific claims in a text, distinguishing claims that are supported by reasons and evidence from claims that are not. **Questions 4, 5: Informational Text 1.** Cite textual evidence to support analysis of what the text says explicitly as well as inferences drawn from the text.

Read the selection. Then answer the questions that follow.

We Need Help!

Dear Editor,	2
Martin Skateboard Park is well worth saving! We need adult volunteers to keep it	16
open.	17
Getting this park took four years of sacrifice. Many of us kids and our parents	32
worked very hard for hundreds of hours. We got approval from the park's board	46
of directors for the space. We raised the money for its construction, and we built it	62
ourselves. Now we need adults to manage the place.	71
The Park Board made us get insurance to cover any accidents. The insurance	84
company insists on having adult supervisors in charge. They know the park can make	98
skateboarding safer. They also want to be sure all skateboarders wear pads and helmets	112
as well as behave in a sensible way.	120
Martin Skateboard Park is truly an awesome place! It has eight ramps that range in	135
levels of difficulty. There are a variety of handrails, ledges, and blocks. It also has a	151
street course to teach off-park skills and safety.	159
We need places to keep kids busy and out of trouble. We must not close this	175
wonderful park!	177
Sincerely,	178
Tabatha Wilson	180

Turn the page.

Answer the questions below.

1 Which of the following is a statement of fact?

  A Martin Skateboard Park is well worth saving.

  (B) Adult volunteers are needed to keep the park open.

  C Completing the park took years of sacrifice.

  D Martin Skateboard Park is an awesome place.

2 Which of the following is a statement of opinion?

  F The Park Board required insurance to cover any accidents.

  G The insurance company insists that adult supervisors be present.

  (H) Martin Skateboard Park is an awesome place.

  J The eight ramps in the park vary in difficulty.

3 Which of the following tells you that Tabatha is a young person who uses the park?

  (A) She uses the phrase "us kids and our parents."

  B She writes a lot about the Park Board.

  C She mentions the insurance company.

  D She signs the letter using her first name.

4 What information in the letter bests supports the claim that "the park can make skateboarding safer"?

Possible responses: The park has a street course that teaches skills and safety. The adult supervision will help make it safe too.

Common Core State Standards

Questions 1, 2, 4: Informational Text 8. Trace and evaluate the argument and specific claims in a text, distinguishing claims that are supported by reasons and evidence from claims that are not. **Question 3: Informational Text 1.** Cite textual evidence to support analysis of what the text says explicitly as well as inferences drawn from the text.

Name _____

Read the selection. Then answer the questions that follow.

The Wonder of Winter

I got sentimental while Roberto and I were out shoveling a couple of feet of snow	16
surrounding the family car. I related how, when I was his age, the other boys and I	33
would build daring slopes along the riverbank. We'd pour water on the slopes to freeze	48
them. They'd endure for weeks. Today's snow was the heaviest in years, but it will only	64
last a week or so before it melts away.	73
While inside, warming up for another go at shoveling, I read some of my favorite	88
winter poems and writings to Roberto. William Wordsworth wrote a wonderful poem	100
about his memories ice-skating at Hawkshead. He wrote about skating at night on the	114
lake near his boyhood school in England.	121
John Greenleaf Whittier was snowbound in New England. He and his family	133
tunneled through deep snow to feed some animals. Then they huddled around a fire as	148
the heavy, silent blanket piled high against their house.	157
Henry David Thoreau kept a fascinating journal and told about his long, rugged	170
cross-country skating trips on frozen streams in New England.	179
Finally, I read Robert Frost's poem about stopping with his horse to watch the woods	194
fill up with snow.	198
"I guess we should go finish digging out the car," Roberto said dreamily, staring out	213
the window. I thought I saw a special light in his eyes. They reflected the old promise	230
that a new snowfall holds.	235

Turn the page.

Answer the questions below.

1 **Which of the following is a statement of opinion?**

   A   The family car was buried under a couple of feet of snow.

   (B) The slopes the main character and his friends built were daring.

   C   The main character read some of his favorite descriptions of winter.

   D   Wordsworth's memories were from Hawkshead.

2 **Which of the following is a statement of fact?**

   F   Thoreau's exciting journal described a fascinating cross-country skating trip.

   G   There was a special light in Roberto's eyes.

   H   Today's snow will only last a week or so.

   (J) Whittier and his family tunneled through snow.

3 **Why did the main character read to Roberto?**

   A   to avoid the unpleasant task of digging out the car

   (B) to recall pleasant visions of winter weather

   C   to illustrate how boys were braver when he was young

   D   to teach Roberto that he should read more poetry

4 **The main character's description of how he helped make a slope for sledding when he was a boy supports his opinion that**

   F   Roberto was not enjoying the snow.

   G   winter was getting more severe each year.

   (H) shoveling snow can bring back pleasant memories.

   J   only famous writers can appreciate winter.

5 **The main character summarizes four writing samples that illustrate winter sentiments. Given the examples, what is the main character's opinion of winter?**

Possible responses: The main character expresses winter as a season full of wonder, instilling the idea in Roberto. The main character has pleasant memories about the season from his own childhood. He has also read a lot about winter.

⌐ **Common Core State Standards** \

Questions 1, 2, 4: Informational Text 8. Trace and evaluate the argument and specific claims in a text, distinguishing claims that are supported by reasons and evidence from claims that are not. **Questions 3, 5: Informational Text 1.** Cite textual evidence to support analysis of what the text says explicitly as well as inferences drawn from the text.

- -

Read the selection. Then answer the questions that follow.

Still Some Concerns

When the group of parents and children who championed having a public skateboard	13
park began lobbying the City Council to build one, we began to have serious concerns.	28
Sure, a skateboard park seemed to be an interesting idea. Clearly, the city had plenty	43
of space in any one of several city parks. Yet we wanted to weigh the other costs. We	61
praised the Council's questions of caution: How many children would use such a park?	75
Was the cost a wise investment of public money?	84
However, neither the Council nor *The Journal Times* fully appreciated the	95
community's enthusiasm over the park. The parents and children raised the money	107
needed to cover its construction. Then, perhaps too quickly, the Council approved using	120
space in Martin Park.	124
The problem is that building the park was not the only cost. As we suggested back	140
then, skateboarding is not an accident-free sport. Some studies suggest there are no	153
more accidents in skateboarding than in other sports, but that skateboarding tends to	166
result in more serious injuries. Sliding on a skateboard along hand rails mounted in	180
cement does seem risky. The Council eventually recognized that there were risks for	193
the city. But it was too late. The park was built. The only solution has been getting	210
expensive insurance to cover any lawsuits over accidents. Now the insurance company	222
has insisted on continual adult supervision of activities at the park. They want to avoid	237
accidents.	238
So far, there are not enough adults willing to supervise the place, so the park has	254
not reopened. One wonders what has happened to all the supportive adults who first	268
helped build the park. Why haven't they stepped up to fill this requirement? Maybe the	283
possibility of accidents worries them too.	289

Turn the page.

Answer the questions below.

1 Which of the following from the selection is a statement of fact?

   A A skateboard park seemed like an interesting idea.

   B The city had plenty of space in any one of several city parks.

   (C) The kids and their parents raised the money to fund its construction.

   D The Council approved using space in Martin Park too quickly.

2 Which of the following from the selection is a statement of opinion?

   (F) Sliding along hand rails mounted in cement is risky.

   G The Council recognized that there were risks for the city.

   H The insurance company has insisted on continual adult supervision.

   J There are not enough adults willing to supervise the place.

3 Which detail in the selection supports the statement that building the park was not the only expense?

   A The people who wanted the park raised the money to build it.

   B It was not clear how many kids would use the park.

   (C) The Council obtained insurance to cover any lawsuits over accidents.

   D Too few adults had volunteered to act as supervisors in the park.

4 What opinion in the selection is supported by the studies about accidents?

Skateboarding can lead not just to accidents but to injuries more serious than those in other sports.

5 What do you think is the author's purpose for writing this selection?

Answers may vary. Possible response: The author's purpose is to air concerns about reopening the skateboarding park.

Common Core State Standards

Questions 1–4: Informational Text 8. Trace and evaluate the argument and specific claims in a text, distinguishing claims that are supported by reasons and evidence from claims that are not. **Question 5: Informational Text 1.** Cite textual evidence to support analysis of what the text says explicitly as well as inferences drawn from the text.

Name _____

Read the selection. Then answer the questions that follow.

Ashlee's Second Song

In 2004, on a live TV show, singer Ashlee Simpson began to sing her second song as | 17
planned. It turned out to be the same song she had sung earlier that night. Noticing the | 34
mistake, she stopped moving her lips. Her voice went right on singing. | 46

Someone behind the scenes had put on the wrong recording for Ashlee to lip-synch | 60
(move her lips along with the words but not actually sing out loud). Because the show | 76
was live, Ashlee was supposed to be singing. Ashlee was embarrassed and ended her | 90
performance. | 91

Reporters called this Ashlee's "Milli Vanilli Moment." Milli Vanilli was a popular | 103
singing group of two young men. In public performances, they lip-synched to the | 116
voices of other singers—the singers who had made Milli Vanilli's recordings. When | 129
the group was discovered to have been lip-synching all along, their singing careers | 142
were over. | 144

It doesn't seem fair to ruin Ashlee's career. People have been lip-synching for a long | 159
time. Famous movie stars in musicals had to lip-synch if their singing voices were bad. | 174
At least Ashlee was lip-synching to a recording of her own voice. | 186

Turn the page.

Answer the questions below.

1 The topic of this selection is

  A Milli Vanilli.

  (B) lip-synching.

  C musicals.

  D actors who sing.

2 What is the main idea of this selection?

  F Ashlee Simpson's career is ruined.

  G Ashlee Simpson only recorded one song.

  (H) Lip-synching is more common than we think.

  J People might prefer to see singers lip-synch.

3 Which detail in the selection supports the argument that Simpson's action should not ruin her career?

  A Someone else was responsible for playing the wrong song.

  B Simpson was supposed to be singing because the show was live.

  (C) Simpson was lip-synching to a recording of her own voice.

  D Pop group Milli Vanilli had been lip-synching all their songs.

4 Based on the selection, what could happen as a result of lip-synching?

Possible response: Lip-synching could ruin a singer's credibility or career. People may not be willing to pay money to attend the concerts of singers who may be lip-synching during their performances.

Common Core State Standards

Questions 1, 2: Informational Text 2. Determine a central idea of a text and how it is conveyed through particular details; provide a summary of the text distinct from personal opinions or judgments. **Question 3: Informational Text 8.** Trace and evaluate the argument and specific claims in a text, distinguishing claims that are supported by reasons and evidence from claims that are not. **Question 4: Informational Text 1.** Cite textual evidence to support analysis of what the text says explicitly as well as inferences drawn from the text.

Name _____

Read the selection. Then answer the questions that follow.

Familiar Faces

Long before photography became available to the public in 1839, people obtained	12
portraits from painters. Painters often earned a living doing portraits of family	24
members, royalty, and people who could afford their own likenesses on canvas.	36
Painters sometimes chose to paint people who were not well-known. In the 1600s	49
Jan Vermeer of Delft, Holland, painted women who appeared to be living or working	63
in his house. One such painting is called *Girl with a Pearl Earring.* The model remains	79
a mystery. Art historians do not know who she was. In 1999 a novel based on research	96
and imagined details about this unknown girl, Vermeer, and the painting was published.	109
The novel was so popular it was made into a movie.	120
In two famous oil portraits, the subjects are wearing hats. One, by Vermeer, is called	135
Girl with a Red Hat. The girl peers right at the viewer from under a very bright	152
red-orange hat that catches the light on its top. The brim of the hat shadows her eyes so	170
the light strikes just the lower half of her face. The other is Thomas Sully's *The Torn*	187
Hat, a painting made around 1820 of his young son outdoors. The boy's rosy face is lit	204
beneath a large straw hat with a downturned brim. The straw brim is partly torn away	220
from the crown of the hat, letting mellow sunlight fall on just one area of the boy's	237
face. These effects of light and shadow are very pleasing to the eye.	250
Many well-known portraits are now available as framed prints, posters, postcards, and	262
calendars. Most of the subjects were not famous during their time, but the painters who	277
chose them made the faces of their subjects famous and beloved throughout the world.	291

Turn the page.

Answer the questions below.

1 Which of the following is a generalization you can make from this selection?

(**A**) Many paintings are of people who wanted to see their likenesses on canvas.

B Artists hope their lives will be made into movies.

C Very few famous portraits have been made with figures wearing hats.

D Most famous portraits include someone wearing a hat.

2 Another title for this selection could be

F "Hats in Paintings."

G "The Work of Vermeer."

(**H**) "Subjects in Art."

J "The Role of Light in Paintings."

3 What is the main idea of this selection?

A Long before photography, people had portraits painted of themselves.

B A novelist writing about Vermeer made up details about his life.

C Famous portraits are usually of someone in the painter's household.

(**D**) Some portraits are widely reproduced many years after being painted.

4 Which detail in the selection shows that unknown subjects of famous paintings can still excite curiosity?

F Painters sometimes chose to paint people who were not well known to the public.

G The shadow from a hat brim partly hides the girl's face in one Vermeer oil portrait.

H People working in painters' houses often could not afford portraits of themselves.

(**J**) A popular novel was written about the imagined story of Vermeer and a girl he painted.

5 What is the purpose of the hat in *Girl with a Red Hat* and *The Torn Hat*?

Possible response: The artists used the hats to cast shadows on parts of their subjects' faces, creating effects of light and shade that are pleasing to the eye.

/ **Common Core State Standards**

Question 1: Informational Text 1. Cite textual evidence to support analysis of what the text says explicitly as well as inferences drawn from the text.
Questions 2–5: Informational Text 2. Determine a central idea of a text and how it is conveyed through particular details; provide a summary of the text distinct from personal opinions or judgments.

Name _____

Read the selection. Then answer the questions that follow.

Why Is Sue Like a Bird?

No one is suggesting that Sue, the most complete skeleton of a Tyrannosaurus Rex	14
ever unearthed, could fly. Her reconstructed remains at the Field Museum in Chicago	27
are a gigantic forty-two feet long and thirteen feet high at the hip. It is estimated that	44
this dinosaur weighed seven tons!	49
More than two hundred of Sue's bones were uncovered near Faith, South Dakota,	62
in 1990 by fossil hunter Sue Hendrickson. Analysis of the bones indicated that this	76
dinosaur existed near the end of the Cretaceous age about sixty-eight million years ago.	90
Scientists are fascinated by the numerous characteristics about dinosaurs that are	101
similar to those of birds. Sue walked with three toes forward, one toe back, and a claw	118
on each toe, just as most birds do. Like Sue, birds have a neck curved like the letter s	137
and have hollow but strong bones.	143
A distinguishing characteristic of most birds is that they have an unusual wishbone.	156
It is made up of small yet long connected bones running side by side. We aren't sure	173
what a bird's wishbone accomplishes. When some scientists used a special X-ray	185
camera to photograph birds flying in wind tunnels, they learned that the wishbone is	199
stretched wide like a spring when a bird's wings arch downward during flight. It is	214
believed that this helps the bird fill its body with air as it flies. It is not clear, though,	233
what purpose this serves.	237
Sue has a wishbone too. Still, no one has contended that Sue could fly. The	252
similarities between birds and the dinosaur have raised questions. We now wonder how	265
birds today are related to dinosaurs.	271

Turn the page.

Answer the questions below.

1 The topic of this selection is

   A the Field Museum.

   B Sue Hendrickson.

   (C) dinosaurs and birds.

   D wishbones.

2 Which of the following best expresses the selection's main idea?

   F Sue might have been able to fly.

   G A dinosaur weighs about seven tons.

   H A distinguishing characteristic of most birds is a wishbone.

   (J) There appears to be some relationship between birds and dinosaurs.

3 Which of the following best expresses the main idea of paragraph four?

   A Sacs in a bird's body fill with air as it flies.

   (B) The purpose of a bird's wishbone is not clear.

   C The wishbone is stretched wide when a bird's wings arch downward.

   D An X-ray camera was used to photograph flying birds.

4 Based on the selection, do you think any dinosaurs would have been able to fly? Explain your answer.

Possible response: Yes. They were so much like birds. Based on how many things dinosaurs' bodies have in common with modern birds' bodies, I think there probably were some dinosaurs that could fly.

5 What details in the selection make it clear that Sue was not a bird?

Possible response: Her weight and size.

Common Core State Standards

Questions 1–3, 5: **Informational Text 2.** Determine a central idea of a text and how it is conveyed through particular details; provide a summary of the text distinct from personal opinions or judgments. **Question 4: Informational Text 1.** Cite textual evidence to support analysis of what the text says explicitly as well as inferences drawn from the text.

Name _____

Read the selection. Then answer the questions that follow.

Brain Wrinkles

Did you know that when a baby is just beginning to grow inside its mother, its brain	17
is completely smooth? A few months before the birth, wrinkles begin to develop in the	32
baby's brain. The wrinkles our brains have when we are born are the wrinkles we will	48
have for life.	51
Why are our brains wrinkled? Over thousands of years, as humans' thinking grew	64
more complex, their brains grew larger. Their heads, however, stayed about the same	77
size. The brain folded itself to fit into that space. This folding of the brain created	93
ridges and grooves. A ridge is called a **gyrus**. A shallow groove is called a **sulcus**,	109
and a deep groove is called a **fissure**. Some ridges and grooves have their own names	125
because they appear on all healthy human brains. Still, they may look a little different	140
from person to person.	144
Does your brain change throughout your life? Yes and no. It doesn't get new	158
wrinkles, but it does change as you learn new things. Those changes are not visible like	174
the ridges and grooves.	178
Unfolded, your brain would be about as big as a pillowcase. Try sleeping on that!	193

1. Precentral gyrus
2. Central sulcus
3. Postcentral gyrus
4. Lateral (Sylvian) fissure
5. Superior temporal gyrus

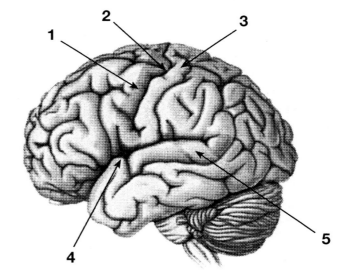

Turn the page.

Answer the questions below.

1 **Why do some grooves and ridges on the human brain have their own names?**

   A They are grouped together in a particular way.

   B They are named for the scientists who discovered them.

   (C) They are common to all healthy human brains.

   D They are different from all the other folds and fissures.

2 **Which sentence would be *best* to add to the end of the third paragraph to summarize its main idea?**

   (F) Scientists believe these changes involve neurons (nerve cells), and that learning increases the connections between them.

   G To better understand human brains, scientists have studied the changes in the brains of animals as they learn new tasks.

   H The fact that our brains undergo some change as we learn and have new experiences means that our brains are "plastic."

   J The connections between the neurons (nerve cells) in the brain are called synapses, and the number of synapses can increase.

3 **Look at the drawing of the human brain. Which arrow points to a fissure?**

   A Arrow 1

   B Arrow 2

   C Arrow 3

   (D) Arrow 4

4 **According to the selection, what is the only visible change a human brain ever goes through?**

The human brain starts out smooth and becomes wrinkled while we are still developing as babies.

Common Core State Standards

Questions 1, 2, 4: Informational Text 1. Cite textual evidence to support analysis of what the text says explicitly as well as inferences drawn from the text. **Informational Text 2.** Determine a central idea of a text and how it is conveyed through particular details; provide a summary of the text distinct from personal opinions or judgments. **Question 3: Informational Text 7.** Integrate information presented in different media or formats (e.g., visually, quantitatively) as well as in words to develop a coherent understanding of a topic or issue.

Name _____

Read the selection. Then answer the questions that follow.

Handedness

Whether you consider yourself right-handed or left-handed, chances are good you're	11
not completely either one. Although we tend to rely on one hand for a careful task like	28
writing, we may habitually use the other hand for easier tasks. In fact, "handedness"	42
refers to more than the hands. It's useful instead to think of your left and right sides,	59
including your ears, eyes, hands, and feet. Which ear do you put a phone to when you	76
answer it? If you've looked through a telescope, which eye did the looking? Which	90
hand do you use to unscrew the lid of a jar and which to screw the lid back on? Which	110
foot do you kick a ball with? The answers may surprise you.	122
Actions for which many humans use either hand are things like carrying a suitcase	136
or holding a leash. Actions for which most humans always use the same hand are skills	152
like hammering, throwing a ball, and writing. Seventy to ninety-five percent of the	165
human population are right-handed. Five to thirty percent are left-handed. And a small	178
percentage can use either hand even for tasks like writing. Amazingly, these ranges are	192
the same for human populations all over the world.	201
Scientists can't explain why so many humans are right-handed. M.K. Holder, a	213
scientist who studies animals, has found that some gorillas, chimps, and monkeys in the	227
wild will sometimes prefer one hand over the other for doing certain tasks. However, she	242
has not found that such a preference exists over a whole population, as it does in humans.	259

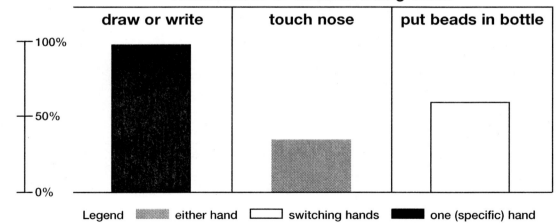

Handedness of Children Doing Tasks

Legend: either hand | switching hands | one (specific) hand

Turn the page.

Answer the questions below.

1 Which of the following *best* expresses the main idea of the first paragraph?

   A People tend to use the same hand for a specific task every time.

   (B) Very few people use only the left hand or the right hand for all tasks.

   C No one knows for certain why most people are mostly right-handed.

   D The majority of humans use their right hands for doing the hard tasks.

2 Based on the chart, which of the following was found?

   (F) Nearly all children used only one hand (either left or right) for drawing.

   G Most children used either hand to touch their noses.

   H Few children switched hands while they were putting beads in a bottle.

   J None of the children switched hands while writing.

3 According to the selection, which task would people be *most likely* to do with either hand?

   A write a letter

   B throw a ball

   (C) hold a leash

   D use a hammer

4 Why might their answers to the questions in the first paragraph "surprise" readers?

   (F) Readers probably think they are entirely right-sided or left-sided.

   G Readers probably write with one hand only and always use the other to eat.

   H Readers probably believe they use their left hand for most tasks.

   J Readers probably use left hands to open jars and right hands to close them.

5 Based on the selection, what difference between handedness in humans and handedness in animals did M.K. Holder observe?

All humans show handedness, whereas only some individual animals seem to show a hand preference.

Common Core State Standards

Questions 1, 3–5: Informational Text 1. Cite textual evidence to support analysis of what the text says explicitly as well as inferences drawn from the text. **Informational Text 2.** Determine a central idea of a text and how it is conveyed through particular details; provide a summary of the text distinct from personal opinions or judgments. **Question 2: Informational Text 7.** Integrate information presented in different media or formats (e.g., visually, quantitatively) as well as in words to develop a coherent understanding of a topic or issue.

Read the selection. Then answer the questions that follow.

The Ugli Fruit

It seems possible, but not certain, that the orange took its name from its color. It	16
is certain that the ugli fruit got its name from its appearance. This cross between an	32
early species of grapefruit and the orange is truly ugly. The ugli fruit can vary in size.	49
Its color is best described as a blotchy yellow, green, and orange. It has ugly scars	65
and pock marks, and the puffy bumps that make it easy to peel give it a very distorted	83
appearance.	84

So why would anyone ever taste the unappetizing-looking ugli fruit? This strange	96
fruit has a delicious pinkish-orange flesh with a sweetly tart, citrus flavor. It can be	111
eaten like a tangerine or cut in half like a grapefruit. It is also very tasty in a variety	130
of salads and desserts. Some people feel that its name is unfair and have wanted to	146
pronounce it *oog'-li* (as in *oodles*).	152

The ugli fruit was discovered in Jamaica. It was not grown on purpose but came	167
about by accident. At first it was unique to Jamaica, but by cultivation and marketing,	182
it spread to Florida in the 1930s. It remains somewhat unusual, and there has been	197
a shortage of it as the demand for the fruit has increased. In addition to this, the ugli	215
harvesting season is short, lasting only from December into April. This results in prices	229
between two and three dollars each, so enjoying the ugli is not inexpensive.	242

Nutrition Facts about the Ugli

(medium-sized)

Calories	35
Calories from Fat	0
Total Fat	0%
Saturated Fat	0%
Sodium 0 mg	0%
Carbohydrates 10 g	3%
Fiber 0 g	0%
Protein 1 g	
High in Vitamins A and C	

Turn the page.

Answer the questions below.

1 Which sentence best states the main idea of this selection?

   A The ugli fruit has an unappetizing appearance.

   B The ugli fruit is a cross between a grapefruit and an orange.

   (C) The ugli fruit may be ugly, but it is tasty.

   D The ugli fruit is costly.

2 Which sentence would be the best opening sentence to state the main idea of the first paragraph?

   F If you ever travel to Jamaica, be sure to try an ugli fruit.

   (G) Looking at the ugli fruit probably won't make you hungry.

   H There is little that is special about the look of an ugli fruit.

   J The ugli fruit has a delicious flavor.

3 Why do some people pronounce the name of the ugli fruit *oog'-li*?

   A This is how it is said in Jamaica, where the fruit came from.

   B This mistake occurs because of the familiar word "oodles."

   C They say it this way because the fruit looks so unusual.

   (D) They think that such a tasty fruit should not be called ugly.

4 Since its discovery in Jamaica, has the ugli's popularity increased or decreased? Use details from the selection to support your answer.

Possible responses: The ugli's popularity has increased. It is now grown in Jamaica and in the United States. There is a shortage because so many people want it.

5 Based on the information in the graphic, would the ugli make a good or bad choice for a breakfast fruit if you were trying to avoid fat and sodium? Explain.

It would be a good choice because it has no fat and no sodium.

Common Core State Standards

Questions 1–4: Informational Text 1. Cite textual evidence to support analysis of what the text says explicitly as well as inferences drawn from the text. **Informational Text 2.** Determine a central idea of a text and how it is conveyed through particular details; provide a summary of the text distinct from personal opinions or judgments. **Question 5: Informational Text 7.** Integrate information presented in different media or formats (e.g., visually, quantitatively) as well as in words to develop a coherent understanding of a topic or issue.

Name _____

Read the selection. Then answer the questions that follow.

A Great Way to Get Around!

We intended to buy ten-gear bicycles. Then we saw the shiny black VeloSolexes	13
silently zipping around the French port city Le Havre. Way back then, they cost only	28
$68 each!	30
With the motor doing the work, we got great views of the beautiful valleys by sitting	46
up straight with both feet up and having the freedom to look all around. The tiny	62
motors rubbing against the front tires propelled us at an ideal viewing speed of fifteen	77
miles an hour. Going up hills we assisted the motor by using the pedals. So we got	94
some of the exercise we had anticipated.	101
In Paris, thousands of Solexes braved the crazy traffic. Out on the open road,	115
however, no other Solexes loaded with camping gear were seen. As we traveled the	129
country on our laden Solexes, the curious French often stopped us with friendly	142
questions.	143
The motor on the Solex didn't always run smoothly. Yet my memory of them is very	159
positive. When I saw an ad the other day that said they are being exported to the United	177
States, I couldn't resist paying close attention.	184

The VeloSolex in America!*

First manufactured in France in 1946, this RETRO-styled transportation is back** in 2006! With answers to lots of problems!

- Over 200 miles per gallon of gas! (Tank holds enough for over 60 miles.)
- The quietest, most dependable motor on the streets!
- Uses **unleaded** gasoline!
- For riders of many ages!

Tres chic! (as they say in France) ONLY $1,299

The VeloSolex weighs only 62 pounds. It is not a moped! It is a **power-assisted** bicycle. Millions have been sold in Europe, China, and other places. . . . AND NOW IT IS AVAILABLE IN THE UNITED STATES!
The Reliable "Solex" can go up to 23 mph on level ground! Power-assisted on hills.

- One-cylindered, two-stroke engine with a friction wheel on the front tire.
- Front and rear brakes, commanded by hand levers.
- Front and rear lights.
- Specialty items available include heated handlebar cuffs.

*Not a replica, but the <u>original</u> 1946 model with an engine modified to run on unleaded fuel with 2-3% oil! Made with the original VeloSolex manufacturing tools!
Available in all 50 states.
**Sold to a moped manufacturer who stopped its production in 1988. It is now being manufactured again under new ownership.

Turn the page.

Answer the questions below.

1 What detail in the ad appears to be contradicted by the selection?

  A The VeloSolex goes over sixty miles on a tank of gas.

  B The rider must assist the motor on hills.

  (C) The motor is the most dependable on the streets.

  D The motor rubs against the front tire.

2 What detail in the ad supports the story's comment about Solexes that impressed the writer in Le Havre?

  F The Solex uses unleaded gasoline.

  G The Solex has hand-controlled front and rear brakes.

  H Solexes are all designed like the 1946 model.

  (J) The Solex motor is the quietest on the streets.

3 Which comment in the ad refers to the VeloSolex's place of origin?

  A "This RETRO-styled transportation is back in 2006!"

  (B) "*Tres Chic!* (as they say in France)"

  C "The VeloSolex weighs only 62 pounds."

  D "Specialty items available include heated handlebar cuffs."

4 What did the speaker most likely think when he saw today's price for a VeloSolex? Explain.

Possible response: He must have been shocked. The VeloSolex sells for almost twenty times as much as he paid for the one he bought in France years earlier.

Common Core State Standards

Questions 1–3: Informational Text 7. Integrate information presented in different media or formats (e.g., visually, quantitatively) as well as in words to develop a coherent understanding of a topic or issue. **Question 4: Informational Text 1.** Cite textual evidence to support analysis of what the text says explicitly as well as inferences drawn from the text.

Read the selection. Then answer the questions that follow.

Knowing Your Stars

The constellations are imaginary patterns of stars that help us identify which star | 13
is which. For more than six thousand years, people have named the patterns that stars | 28
seem to make. Yet those in a particular constellation are usually not close together. | 42
Their relationship that makes the pattern depends on their sizes and distances from us | 56
and on the angle of our view. | 63

Ursa Major, the Big Bear, is shaped something like a bear and is the third-largest of | 79
the eighty-eight constellations. Another that actually looks something like its popular | 90
name, the Little Dipper, is Ursa Minor. However, its pattern of faint stars is not easy to | 107
pick out on a clear night when the sky seems packed with stars. | 120

The Big Dipper, on the other hand, is formed by bright stars and can be identified | 136
fairly easily. It is a part of Ursa Major and is not officially a constellation, but it helps | 154
us locate other stars. The two stars at the end of its bowl are called the pointer stars | 172
because an imaginary line drawn between them points up to Polaris, the relatively faint | 186
North Star. Polaris marks north more accurately than a magnetic compass, so if you are | 201
looking toward it, you are always looking north. | 209

Once you locate Polaris, it's easier to find the Little Dipper because Polaris is at the | 225
end of its long handle. In between the two dippers, the constellation Draco, the dragon, | 240
curves lazily across the sky. Knowing where to look enables you to spot his snakelike | 255
body and his large square-shaped head. There are practical values to recognizing | 267
constellations, but just identifying them makes the night sky much more interesting. | 279

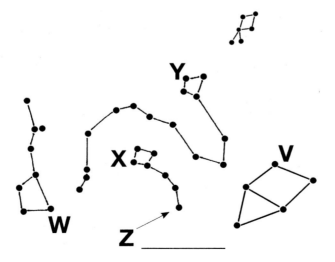

Turn the page.

Answer the questions below.

1 **Compared to Ursa Minor, the Big Dipper is**

A fainter and harder to find.

(B) brighter and easier to find.

C made up of many more stars.

D closer to the North Star.

2 **Which letter on the diagram represents Ursa Major?**

(F) W

G X

H Y

J Z

3 **The Little Dipper is identified on the diagram by which letter?**

A V

B W

(C) X

D Y

4 **What name should be written on the chart by the letter Z?**

F Ursa Major

G Draco

(H) Polaris

J The Big Dipper

5 **If you were going to substitute the name Draco for one of the letters on the diagram, tell which letter you would replace and why you decided that constellation is Draco.**

<u>**Draco would go where the letter Y is because that is the**</u>

<u>**constellation that is long and curvy like a snake and because**</u>

<u>**it is in between the two dippers.**</u>

Copyright © Pearson Education, Inc., or its affiliates. All Rights Reserved. 6

Common Core State Standards

Question 1: Informational Text 1. Cite textual evidence to support analysis of what the text says explicitly as well as inferences drawn from the text.
Questions 2–5: Informational Text 7. Integrate information presented in different media or formats (e.g., visually, quantitatively) as well as in words to develop a coherent understanding of a topic or issue.

Name _____

Read the selection. Then answer the questions that follow.

The Theory of Tectonic Plates

Over the last hundred years, there have been interesting explanations of the Earth's	13
geological wonders revolving around a general tectonic plate theory. It states that	25
the Earth's crust consists of a dozen or more plates that ride on a layer of hot, liquid	43
magma. They slide around, striking and pressing against each other and sometimes	55
allowing eruptions of magma. An ocean basin or a continent, or more commonly both,	69
may ride on a single plate.	75
Before 1912, many believed that the Earth had once been a molten ball, and as	90
it cooled, its cracking surface created its terrains. However, in 1912, a new theory	104
asserted that the world began as one big continent. It broke apart and drifted in different	120
directions. In 1929, another theory suggested that the continents had moved as if on	134
a kind of conveyor belt. They moved because the Earth was always being heated and	149
cooled by the magma escaping from under its crust.	158
By the 1960s, theorists noted that wide, high mountain ridges form on the ocean	172
floor, forcing it to spread out toward the continents while making very deep crevices.	186
This has led to theories about how an ocean plate pressing against a continental plate	201
might slide under it, causing earthquakes.	207
These theories also explain how magma erupts as lava and how heat escaping from	221
the ocean floor's mountains causes the ridges that make the ocean expand. All these	235
ideas are more complex than can be reported in a summary, but it looks as if they fit	253
well within a general tectonic plate theory.	260

Ideas that Tend to Fit the "Tectonic Plate" Theory

Date	Theory Name	Theorists	Comments on the Theory
Before 1912	"Contraction"		The Earth, a molten ball, cracked and folded up on itself as it cooled.
1912	"Continental Drift"	Alfred Wegener	One big continent (Pangaea: *all lands*) broke apart and drifted into the positions of the world's continents today. The leading edges of the continents "encountered resistance" and folded upwards, making mountains.
1929	"Thermal Convection"	Arthur Holmes	Based on Wegener's theory, Holmes's theory proposed that repeated heating and cooling caused by escaping magma caused the continents to move.
1960s	"Sea-floor Spreading"	Howard Hess and R. Deitz	Accepting Holmes's theory, new technologies mapped the ocean's floor, where there were growing and heat-emitting ridges. A deep trench runs along the ocean's length, and this region experiences an elevated number of earthquakes and pushes the floor ever farther apart and slowly against the continents.
Since the 1960s	"Subduction"		When sea-floor spreading presses an ocean plate against a continental plate, the heavier rock of the sea plate slides under the continental plate.
Fairly recently	"The Gaia Theory"	James Lovelock	Lovelock's controversial theory builds on the tectonic plate theory proposing that the Earth is one immense, interacting, and dynamic system. One seismic event can have effects anywhere, even a half a world away.

Turn the page.

Answer the questions below.

1 Which theory was the first to challenge the old theory that the Earth had been a molten ball?
- **A** the "Contraction" theory
- **(B)** the "Continental Drift" theory
- **C** the "Sea-floor Spreading" theory
- **D** the "Subduction" theory

2 Whose theory focused on the happenings at the bottom of the oceans?
- **F** Wegener's
- **G** Holmes's
- **(H)** Hess and Deitz's
- **J** Lovelock's

3 Which idea might most directly explain an earthquake in the state of California?
- **A** "contraction"
- **B** "continental drift"
- **(C)** "subduction"
- **D** "the Gaia theory"

4 Why doesn't a tectonic plate theory contradict Alfred Wegener's theory?

Wegener said that the continents drifted into their positions, and the continents could have drifted because they broke into the tectonic plates.

5 What did Arthur Holmes's theory add to Alfred Wegener's?

Holmes's theory explained what might have caused the continents to drift.

Common Core State Standards

Questions 1–5: Informational Text 7. Integrate information presented in different media or formats (e.g., visually, quantitatively) as well as in words to develop a coherent understanding of a topic or issue.

Name _____

Read the selection. Then answer the questions that follow.

Field or Stage?

After practice that day, the coach offered Edmundo the position of starting	12
linebacker. His best friend, Kai, was going to be the quarterback. So if Edmundo	26
decided to play football, he and Kai would be teammates.	36
Making this decision would be tough for Edmundo. West Eicher's drama club was	49
about to start rehearsals for a rap musical called "Why Cinco de Mayo?" about the	64
significance of that holiday. Edmundo loved the feeling he got from performing. He	77
dreamed of becoming many things, but being an actor or singer was at the top. At the	94
same time, he looked for ways to express pride in his Mexican heritage. He had been	110
offered the starring role. The problem was that rehearsals and football practice were	123
scheduled at the same time.	128
"I'm feeling really strong. Maybe I can do both," he told Kai after practice. "Being	143
teammates would be fun."	147
"Performing would also be fun for you," Kai pointed out. "I know deciding will be	162
hard." He gave Edmundo's shoulder a friendly squeeze. "We'll be friends either way."	175

Turn the page.

Answer the questions below.

1 What was Edmundo doing at the beginning of the story?
- **A** rehearsing for the musical
- **B** trying out for the musical
- **(C)** having football practice
- **D** talking to Kai

2 Edmundo's choice was between getting to be his best friend's teammate or
- **F** playing the quarterback position.
- **G** celebrating Cinco de Mayo.
- **H** working out at football practice.
- **(J)** singing and acting onstage.

3 Why couldn't Edmundo be on the football team and also be in the musical?
- **A** The coach demands that players focus on football only.
- **(B)** Football practice and rehearsals are at the same time.
- **C** Football might damage his singing voice.
- **D** Edmundo would not have time to do homework.

4 One of the ways Edmundo could affect people is by helping the team have a winning season. What other way could Edmundo affect people?

Answers may vary. Possible response: He could be in the musical and share his pride in his Mexican heritage with the audience.

Common Core State Standards

Questions 1–4: Literature 1. Cite textual evidence to support analysis of what the text says explicitly as well as inferences drawn from the text.
Literature 3. Describe how a particular story's or drama's plot unfolds in a series of episodes as well as how the characters respond or change as the plot moves toward a resolution.

Name _____

Read the selection. Then answer the questions that follow.

A Ride on the Mountaineer

The two-day tour on one of Canada's Rocky Mountaineer trains was one I'll always | 14
remember. We boarded at Vancouver in British Columbia on a Tuesday in April. The | 28
same day, trains left Banff and Calgary, heading westward toward Vancouver. | 39

Like proud parents, the Mountaineer staff do not want passengers to miss any of | 53
the view, so the tour proceeds only in daylight. We stopped overnight at Kamloops, | 67
halfway along the route. In the morning, we took the part of the train going to Lake | 84
Louise and Banff, in Alberta. | 89

On the train, the sense of protected comfort inside and the beauty rolling by | 103
outside was pleasant. It was like lounging in a little hotel suspended in a cable car. In | 120
the bubble observation car, I turned 360 degrees around to see the spectacular view | 134
surrounding me, and I felt like a virtual camera. But as we wended our way, I reminded | 151
myself that those high sentinels spreading their white capes all around me were real | 165
mountains, not travel posters. | 169

They were immensely comforting, like silent judges on some very supreme court. | 181
Their robes spread downward into the valleys on either side of the track, where a | 196
green carpet of firs covered their feet. Just below us near the tracks, a somewhat | 211
indifferent inspector was checking out the train. A huge moose stood before us as | 225
we paused in a pass. | 230

Near Banff, we could expect a breathtaking jewel, the emerald Lake Louise. But | 243
first, while staying overnight in Kamloops, I stared out my hotel window like a child | 258
expecting gifts. I promised myself that I'd take the longer tour next time. Then I could | 274
have days to set off into the mountains ("scampering," they call it) expecting to see | 289
grizzly bears, eagles, and cougars. | 294

Turn the page.

- -

Answer the questions below.

1 The staff who plan the Mountaineer tours are compared to
  (A) proud parents.
  B train conductors.
  C jewels.
  D children.

2 When will the author get to see more wildlife in the Canadian Rockies?
  F after he reaches Kamloops
  G when he goes tracking for moose
  H once he gets film for his camera
  (J) on another tour at some later time

3 How does the author feel about all the things to see in that part of Canada?
  A like a weary traveler
  B like someone's parent
  (C) like an excited child
  D like an old judge

4 The "indifferent inspector" in this selection is
  F an employee of the Mountaineer tours.
  G one of the Mountaineer trains.
  (H) a huge moose.
  J the writer himself.

5 What aspect of the view from the observation car makes the author feel like a virtual camera?

  Possible response: The fact that he can turn all the way around in a circle and that there is always a view makes him feel like a virtual camera.

Common Core State Standards

Questions 1, 2, 4: Informational Text 1. Cite textual evidence to support analysis of what the text says explicitly as well as inferences drawn from the text.
Questions 3, 5: Informational Text 6. Determine an author's point of view or purpose in a text and explain how it is conveyed in the text.

Name _____

Read the selection. Then answer the questions that follow.

An American Game

Roque is an unusual outdoor game that is not played in many places these days. Like | 16

croquet, the object of the game is to use a wooden mallet to hit one or two balls in the | 36

correct order through a series of metal hoops called wickets. When the croquet yard | 50

game was brought to the United States from England and Ireland in the late 1800s, | 65

however, someone changed the game considerably. Someone gave it a new set of rules, | 79

a different course, and different equipment. It was so different from croquet that the | 93

name was changed too, by dropping the *c* and the *t*. | 104

Croquet had been played in the Summer Olympics in Paris in 1900, the only time | 119

croquet was an Olympic sport. The French won. The Olympics were in St. Louis in | 134

1904, and roque was included in those competitions. The three medal winners were all | 148

Americans that time. | 151

There are distinctive differences between roque and croquet. The roque mallet is | 163

shorter and heavier, the balls are made of rubber not wood, and the ten wickets are | 179

narrower. Around the outside of a hexagonal course, which has a firm surface instead of | 194

the grass used for the rectangular croquet course, there is a short wall often lined with | 210

rubber. The game involves *caroming,* or banking, the ball off that wall bumper to angle | 225

it at the wickets. So roque is like a cross between croquet and pool or billiards. Many | 242

believe roque takes more skill than croquet. | 249

Like croquet, roque was a part of only one Summer Olympics, for it did not gain | 265

much popularity anywhere. Although roque is still played in the U.S. Midwest, | 277

Americans had returned to croquet by the 1920s. | 285

Turn the page.

Answer the questions below.

1 In what way are the games croquet and roque alike?
(A) The object of the game is the same.
B They both use similarly sized mallets.
C The width of the wickets are the same.
D The shape of the courses are similar.

2 How are the Olympic histories of the two games alike?
F The competitions were both held in Paris.
G Americans won both the croquet and roque competitions.
(H) Each game was part of only one Olympics.
J The same teams competed in 1900 and 1904.

3 When were the rules for roque created?
A before croquet became popular in England and Ireland
(B) after croquet had come to America
C before croquet came to America
D sometime after the 1920s

4 What requirement would make roque more difficult to set up in a typical backyard than croquet?

Roque requires a rubber wall to carom the balls off.

5 Explain why and how it is believed we got the name *roque* for the game.

The new rules made the game different from croquet. The name of the game was changed because roque was different enough from croquet. The letters *c* and *t* were dropped to form roque.

Common Core State Standards

Questions 1–5: Informational Text 1. Cite textual evidence to support analysis of what the text says explicitly as well as inferences drawn from the text.

Name _____

Read the selection. Then answer the questions that follow.

Patterns of Antlers

In springtime, male deer shed their antlers and grow new ones. New antlers grow	14
quickly, usually reaching full size by the end of July. They are covered with fine hair,	30
which the deer removes by rubbing the antlers against tree trunks. The first antlers	44
are short and bear one point; they are shaped like an almost straightened finger. The	59
second set is longer but still bears one point, and a slight curve appears. By the third	76
set, patterns begin to emerge. The third set may be an elongated, more curved "finger,"	91
or it may have one fork, where each antler branches in two directions (two points), one	107
growing longer than the other, or it may have two forks (three points), where, past the	123
fork, one branch forks again.	128
Antlers can grow to have as many as 22 points, and they are most often *symmetrical*	144
(same pattern on both sides).	149

Antler Patterns

Year 1 Year 2 Year 3 Year 4 Year 5

Turn the page.

Answer the questions below.

1 Based on the diagram, how are the Year 3 antler patterns different from those of the other years shown?

(A) Year 3 antlers can have one to three points.

B Year 3 antlers always have three points.

C Year 3 antlers can have just one point.

D Year 3 antlers always have just one fork.

2 At the end of what month would all the male deer be likely to have full-grown antlers?

F April

G May

H June

(J) July

3 Based on the diagram, what can you conclude about a deer's antlers?

A Most Year 3 antlers have two points.

B By Year 4, the fine cover of hair is mostly gone.

C Antlers get weaker as they grow taller.

(D) The base of the antler grows thicker over time.

4 Look at the diagram of antler patterns. Would a deer be *likely* to have one pattern 5a antler and one pattern 5b antler? Explain your answer, based upon the selection.

Possible response: A deer would not be likely to have one pattern 5a antler and one pattern 5b antler because the patterns are not *symmetrical*. A deer's antlers usually have the same pattern for both antlers.

6 Copyright © Pearson Education, Inc., or its affiliates. All Rights Reserved.

Common Core State Standards

Questions 1, 3, 4: Informational Text 7. Integrate information presented in different media or formats (e.g., visually, quantitatively) as well as in words to develop a coherent understanding of a topic or issue. **Question 2: Informational Text 1.** Cite textual evidence to support analysis of what the text says explicitly as well as inferences drawn from the text.

Name _____

Read the selection. Then answer the questions that follow.

Saying No to Soda?

Americans of all ages have loved soda pop since the 1940s. Soda is beloved in part | 16
because it's a symbol of our history. Certain brands have been around so long, they've | 31
become part of American culture. Advertising works hard to keep us in love. We | 45
encounter soda ads in stores, malls, museums, gas stations, and even schools, despite | 58
the fact that soda pop is not a nutritious drink for children. | 70

Studies have shown that American children start out drinking healthy beverages like | 82
milk and, as they become teenagers, switch mostly to soda. The Center for Science in | 97
the Public Interest (CSPI) reports that in 1977–78, boys consumed more than twice as | 112
much soda as milk, while girls consumed more milk than soda. By 1994–96, both boys | 128
and girls consumed twice as much soda as milk. | 137

Soda contributes nothing to our diets and has been shown to have negative effects | 151
on health. Heavy soda drinking is associated with lower intake of vitamins, minerals, | 164
and fiber. Fortunately, since 2000, the allure of soda has slowly begun to fade. This is | 180
in part because bottled water, sports drinks, and energy drinks are now on the market. | 195
It's also because American attitudes toward health and healthy living have changed. | 207
People feel better about choosing water or energy drinks, even though the latter are | 221
high in calories and sugar. Despite the drop in soda consumption, soda remains the U.S. | 236
beverage of choice. | 239

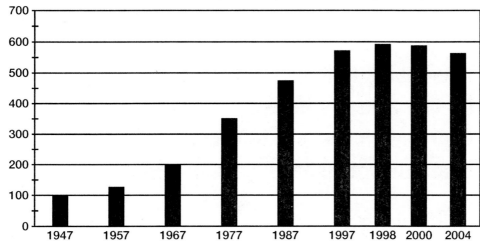

Cans of Soda Produced per Person Annually

Turn the page.

Answer the questions below.

1 The main idea of the *second* paragraph is that

A girls generally drink much less soda than boys do.

B by 1996, girls drank as much milk and soda as boys.

C the CSPI keeps track of American soda consumption.

(D) teenagers have substituted soda for healthier drinks.

2 Based on the chart, which pattern describes soda production between 1997 and 2004?

(F) up then down

G down then up

H steadily down

J steadily up

3 Based on the chart, the greatest increase in the amount of soda produced per person occurred between

A 1947 and 1957.

B 1957 and 1967.

(C) 1967 and 1977.

D 1977 and 1987.

4 According to the chart, *about* how many cans of soda were produced per person in 1997?

F 650

(G) 600

H 550

J 500

5 From the selection and the chart, *about how much* soda do you think was produced in 2002? Explain your answer.

Possible response: I think that soda production in 2002 was still close to 575–600 cans per person. It would be a little lower than in 2000 and higher than in 2004 because the selection says that production has been slowly decreasing since 2000.

6 Copyright © Pearson Education, Inc., or its affiliates. All Rights Reserved.

Common Core State Standards

Questions 1: Informational Text 1. Cite textual evidence to support analysis of what the text says explicitly as well as inferences drawn from the text.
Questions 2–5: Informational Text 7. Integrate information presented in different media or formats (e.g., visually, quantitatively) as well as in words to develop a coherent understanding of a topic or issue.

Read the selection. Then answer the questions that follow.

The Birthday Gift

For his birthday, Harold got a computer desk that came with five separate panels, a bag of screws, and instructions for assembly.

The Simplex Quick-Space Computer Desk 5-14—Assembly Instructions

The desk comes partially assembled, and finishing it is a simple task of four easy steps:

1. Identify the five panels with the letters A–E temporarily affixed to them and the pouch of fourteen screws—six 2-inch screws and eight $1\frac{3}{4}$-inch screws and a hex wrench.

2. Insert the six longer screws into the predrilled holes using the hex wrench to attach sides (Panels B and C) to the back (Panel A). **Be sure the dark side of each panel faces inward.** The metal rails already attached to Panels B and C should be inside and closer to the top. Note that these three panels go together to allow space behind the desk to hide cords.

3. Insert the eight shorter screws into the predrilled holes to attach the computer shelf (Panel D) to the desk. Two of these screws go through Panel A from the back of the desk. The shelf will sit between the two rows of oblong holes precut in Panel A that accommodate thick electrical cords. An extra pair of hands is helpful to complete this step.

4. Slide in the keyboard and mouse shelf (Panel E) with the metal wheel assembly already attached. It snaps into the metal rails on Panel B and Panel C about three inches below Panel D. It should roll easily inward and outward.

Now place your monitor and printer on top of your desk and your computer on the floor underneath your desktop. Now you are **ready to compute!**

| 15 |
| 22 |
| 30 |
| 45 |
| 46 |
| 62 |
| 75 |
| 77 |
| 92 |
| 109 |
| 123 |
| 139 |
| 147 |
| 160 |
| 176 |
| 192 |
| 206 |
| 211 |
| 225 |
| 241 |
| 252 |
| 256 |
| 263 |
| 269 |
| 273 |
| 278 |

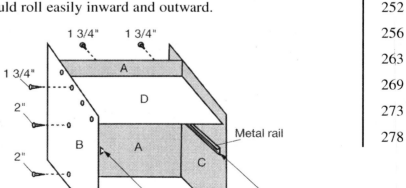

Turn the page.

Answer the questions below.

1 Why do you think the manufacturer put the numbers "5-14" into the name of the desk?

   A to suggest it should only take five hours and fourteen minutes to put it together

   B to show it is just a number that attracts a buyer's attention

   C to indicate that the desk consists of five panels and fourteen screws

   D to distinguish the desk the company makes from the other four models

2 The metal parts already attached to some of the panels should be

   F fitted together when the shelf is added.

   G on the outside of the desk.

   H near the bottom of the desk.

   J removed before finishing the desk.

3 What does this computer desk not have?

   A a shelf for the monitor

   B holes to run the cords through

   C a special shelf for the computer itself

   D room to hide the wires behind it

4 Looking at the diagram, explain how the fit of the sides (Panels B and C) to the back (Panel A) will allow space to hide computer cords.

When the side panels are screwed onto the back panel, the overlapping creates space between the back of the desk and the wall behind it. The cords are then hidden in that space.

5 When Harold uses his desk, where are the panels located in relation to his legs?

Panel D is over Harold's legs. Panels B and C are on the sides and Panel A is in front of his legs.

Common Core State Standards

Questions 1–5: Informational Text 7. Integrate information presented in different media or formats (e.g., visually, quantitatively) as well as in words to develop a coherent understanding of a topic or issue.

Read the selection. Then answer the questions that follow.

How Those Things Work

The Wingarts' garage was full of everyday things made mysterious by dust. One	13
June when the Wingart twins were twelve years old, they went rummaging through	26
some of it.	29
"Let's construct a time machine!" Anton suggested.	36
Herb agreed as he uncovered a motorless riding mower.	45
"We'll travel forward and reveal the rest of the summer," Anton said. "Or should we	60
drift back to last summer?"	65
"We can go a lot farther than that," Herb said.	75
They used cardboard boxes, tape, and old wallpaper rolls. The machine looked	87
scientific in the dark of the garage, but it wouldn't leap time, no matter how many magic	104
words they uttered. Still, they sat and predicted what would happen that summer. . . .	120

*   *   *

Through with college and home for one last summer, the Wingart twins discovered	133
the time machine still sitting in the garage. They laughed hard at it, and then Anton	149
climbed aboard and made a noise like a jet motor.	159
"Remember the great times we had back then?" he said.	169
"Yes," Herb said, taking a seat on the riding mower. They spent an hour recalling	184
that summer, being twelve, and all the adventures they'd had.	194
"You know," Anton said, "this machine works after all. It took us back ten years!"	209

Turn the page.

Answer the questions below.

1 **What does the row of asterisks in the middle of this story represent?**

   A   that the time machine is about to work

   (B)   that years have passed

   C   that the twins are thinking really hard

   D   that time has drifted backward

2 **When does the end of the story actually take place?**

   F   the same summer in which the story begins

   G   the summer before the one in which the story begins

   H   next summer, a year after the summer in which the story begins

   (J)   ten years after the summer in which the story begins

3 **The climax of this story is when**

   A   the twins discover the old riding mower.

   B   the time machine doesn't work.

   C   the twins discover the machine is still in the garage.

   (D)   one twin remarks that the machine worked after all.

4 **Explain what Anton meant when he said the time machine worked.**

**The time machine worked because it brought back many
memories of the summer in which they built it.**

_____

_____

_____

_____

_____

_____

_____

_____

Common Core State Standards

Questions 1, 2, 4: Literature 1. Cite textual evidence to support analysis of what the text says explicitly as well as inferences drawn from the text.
Question 3: Literature 3. Describe how a particular story's or drama's plot unfolds in a series of episodes as well as how the characters respond or change as the plot moves toward a resolution.

Name _____

Read the selection. Then answer the questions that follow.

Pale Male and Lola

In December of 2004, some famous residents were forced to leave 927 Fifth Avenue	14
in New York City. The red tail hawk Pale Male and his mate, Lola, had moved into their	32
digs on the ledge of the twelfth floor more than a decade earlier.	45

The couple had built an eight-foot-long nest on the ledge, and had hatched more	59
than two dozen offspring over the years. But some of the human residents of 927	74
complained about the hawks dropping leftovers of their meals in the street below. Some	88
complained about birdwatchers peering through binoculars at their building. They had	99
voted to have the nest removed, in the hope that the birds would move across the street	116
to the park.	119

The hawk couple's upcoming "eviction" won the attention of New Yorkers, some	131
of whom gathered in Central Park across the street to protest. For years, interested	145
observers had easily identified Pale Male by his unusually white feathers and paused to	159
watch him spin and dive to catch prey. Such evidence of nature in the middle of a city	177
was moving and inspiring.	181

As scheduled, workmen raised a scaffold and demolished the nest. For two weeks	194
after the eviction, Pale Male's fans continued to protest. The local Audubon Society	207
wrote the city's mayor, and protesters even confronted some of 927's famous residents	220
on the street.	223

The protesters' efforts were fruitful. By December 29, a twelve-foot metal apparatus	235
that was constructed to support a new nest had been installed where the old hawk nest	251
had been. It was hoped that Pale Male would be interested in the new arrangement. In	267
the next few weeks, he and Lola were spotted examining the quarters, and everyone	281
awaited a sign that they had decided to move back in.	292

Turn the page.

Answer the questions below.

1 The first event in the sequence of events in the selection appears to have happened sometime in

A January 2005.

B early December 2004.

(C) the 1990s.

D late December 2004.

2 What initiated the public's first awareness of the hawks?

(F) People saw them and were interested in their behavior.

G People used them as an excuse to spy on the residents of 927.

H Word got out that their nest had been demolished.

J Protesters began defending them.

3 What event directly led to the removal of the hawks' nest?

A People began moving out of 927 Fifth Avenue.

B The Audubon Society contacted the mayor.

(C) Residents of 927 cast a vote.

D The hawks' eating habits disturbed residents of 927.

4 What unanswered question in the selection is most important to the outcome?

F Did anyone write a book about Pale Male and Lola?

(G) Did Pale Male and Lola move into the metal nest?

H Were the residents accepting of the birds' possible return?

J Who funded the new metal nest and its placement?

5 What two options for a nest did the hawks have at the end of the selection?

They could live in the metal nest on the ledge of 927 or build a nest across the street in the park.

Common Core State Standards

Questions 1–5: **Informational Text 1.** Cite textual evidence to support analysis of what the text says explicitly as well as inferences drawn from the text. **Informational Text 3.** Analyze in detail how a key individual, event, or idea is introduced, illustrated, and elaborated in a text (e.g., through examples or anecdotes).

Name _____

Read the selection. Then answer the questions that follow.

Ahead by Half

Saturday was unseasonably warm for Iowa in February. People were out bicycling	12
and walking their dogs. Neighbors' windows were open; Dale opened his also and	25
scrutinized his ravaged yard—dark islets of mud in a limitless ocean of snow. Rather	40
than undertake any outdoor activity, Dale committed himself to some interior cleaning.	52
He gathered an assortment of grocery bags and a couple of durable boxes. He began by	68
systematically sorting through drawers of clothes and his many shelves and stacks of	81
books. A faint layer of dust, almost like silt, lay along the recesses of each bookshelf.	97
He sneezed and dusted and vacuumed, and sneezed some more. By midafternoon, Dale	110
had filled two bags with clothing and both boxes with books. "Two and two, pretty	125
good," he reflected.	128
Dale loaded his truck and headed to the local thrift store. Under the carport for	143
drop-offs, he stopped and helped the attendant carry everything inside.	153
"Pretty nice out today," the attendant said, obviously wishing he were elsewhere.	165
"Yes," Dale said. "For some reason it made me want to clean."	177
Unfortunately, it also made Dale want to shop. He parked his car and wandered	191
idly inside.	193
He quickly noted the barely worn winter boots, and appealing all-wool sweaters.	205
Finally, cradling a light armload of two pairs of jeans, a fringed 1920s jacket he would	221
probably never have occasion to wear, and three cotton tee shirts bearing superheroes,	234
he found himself near the bookshelves. He chose several.	243
Once home, Dale used one grocery bag and one box to get his new things into the	260
house. . . . He came out ahead by half.	267

Turn the page.

Answer the questions below.

1 **When did Dale decide it was a good day to clean?**
  A the first thing after waking up on Saturday
  B before going to bed Friday night
  (C) after seeing how nice the weather was
  D upon returning home from a shopping trip

2 **Which of the following occurs first in the selection?**
  F The dust in the house makes Dale sneeze.
  (G) The neighbors' windows are open.
  H Dale looks at the muddy backyard.
  J Dale's own windows are opened.

3 **Which of the following describes the order in which Dale appears to have shopped?**
  A sweaters, blankets, jeans
  (B) boots, tee shirts, books
  C wall art, books, jeans
  D sweaters, vintage jackets, blankets

4 **Explain how Dale came out ahead by half.**

Dale took two grocery bags and two boxes into the thrift store and came home with one bag and one box full of items. So, in terms of cleaning the house and getting rid of things, Dale was "ahead" by "half" of the original amount.

5 **Why might Dale's yard, based on the author's description of it, have inspired Dale to clean his house?**

Answers may vary. Possible response: The yard is muddy and messy, and there is nothing Dale can do about it. Dale can, however, do something about the messiness inside of the house.

/ **Common Core State Standards**

Questions 1–4: Literature 1. Cite textual evidence to support analysis of what the text says explicitly as well as inferences drawn from the text. **Question 5: Literature 3.** Describe how a particular story's or drama's plot unfolds in a series of episodes as well as how the characters respond or change as the plot moves toward a resolution.

Name _____

Read the selection. Then answer the questions that follow.

Getting the Message

Megan's older sister Tess was devastated by her cell phone bill. "I can't pay $100 to	16
use my cell phone!" she lamented.	22
Megan disliked cell phones. It was against the rules to bring one to school, and it	38
pleased her when Eddie Wilson's phone ratted on him during homeroom by ringing	51
loudly inside his backpack.	55
Megan resented people walking along the street seemingly talking to themselves.	66
"Can't they go anywhere alone?" Megan wondered. "When was the last time they heard	80
a bird sing? Would they hear a car horn and know to get out of the way?"	97
Now Tess was into "texting"—using her phone's dinky keyboard to send written	110
messages to friends. "I know I'm charged ten cents a message," Tess wailed, "but it	125
costs the same to read one as to send one, and it adds up fast!"	140
"You recall that agreement you signed when you got your phone?" Megan asked.	153
"Well, maybe reading the 'immediate messages' you get on it will teach you to read the	169
small print when you sign contracts."	175

Turn the page.

Answer the questions below.

1 Which generalization appears to be the theme of this story?

  A Talking things over is never a bad idea.

  B Don't spend more money than you have.

  C Never cross a street while talking on a cell phone.

  (D) Always read a contract through before signing it.

2 Which of these generalizations would Megan be most likely to make?

  F Everyone who has a cell phone has a large monthly bill.

  (G) Cell phones distract most people from the real world.

  H Text messages are the only smart use for cell phones.

  J Cell phones can block out all other noises.

3 Which of the following generalizations about cell phones would Tess be least likely to make?

  A Hearing from friends all day long lets you know you're liked.

  B Texting disturbs people around you less than talking does.

  (C) Cell phones allow you to let someone know you'll be late.

  D A large cell phone bill might persuade you to limit text messaging.

4 Explain why Tess's phone bill was bigger than she expected.

Tess didn't recognize how quickly the cost of sent and received messages would mount up.

Common Core State Standards

Questions 1–4: Literature 1. Cite textual evidence to support analysis of what the text says explicitly as well as inferences drawn from the text.

Name _____

Read the selection. Then answer the questions that follow.

A Learning Experience

Billy Jonstan sang rap songs while playing an electric guitar, and everyone at school | 14

treated Billy like a celebrity. Sam, playing the big round lute that had belonged to his | 30

father, had a different impact. Sam sang original ballads he wrote about his favorite | 44

places in town. The lute's "voice" was soft and muted, and no one seemed very eager | 60

to hear Sam perform. However, when Mr. Sargosta, his music teacher, heard Sam, he | 74

encouraged him to record the ballads. | 80

Because he was so young, one studio agreed to charge Sam just $50 an hour for his | 97

recording session. Even with practically no "editing," it would take a minimum of ten | 111

hours. Then producing each disc would cost $2.50, so if Sam ordered a hundred, they | 126

would cost him $250. | 130

Wiping out his $500 savings account required getting his parents' approval, and | 142

Mr. Sargosta agreed to lend Sam $250. So Sam selected twelve of his best songs and | 158

decided in what order to arrange them on the compact disc. | 169

When the recording session was finished, he named the CD simply "Sam." He | 182

persuaded his sister Kim to make a computer file of a photo she'd taken of him to be | 200

used for the cover, and they printed out his lyrics and stapled little booklets together to | 216

go inside the CD jewel cases. | 222

It was wonderfully exciting, but exhausting too. For a couple of months, he took the | 237

CD around to record stores to ask them to sell it and approached disc jockeys to ask | 254

them to play it. Sam was shy, and that part embarrassed him. | 266

His classmates thought making his own CD was extremely cool. After three months, | 279

Sam had sold enough copies at $10 each to pay Mr. Sargosta back and to restore his | 296

bank account. He had learned a lot about producing a CD! | 307

Turn the page.

Answer the questions below.

1   **Except for Mr. Sargosta, how did people at school feel about Sam's music at first?**

    A   Most liked it better than Billy's rap.

    B   Some thought it made Sam a celebrity.

    (C)   No one paid much attention to it.

    D   A few were ready to help produce it.

2   **For Sam, making a CD was**

    (F)   very expensive.

    G   somewhat expensive.

    H   inexpensive.

    J   pretty cheap.

3   **Who was Sam's most consistent fan?**

    A   Sam's father

    B   Billy Jonstan

    (C)   Mr. Sargosta

    D   Kim

4   **From the story, it can be assumed that producing a successful CD is**

    F   a lot of luck and a little work.

    (G)   a lot of luck and a lot of work.

    H   likely if the music is good.

    J   impossible without sound editing.

5   **How did Sam feel about his music? What makes you think this?**

Possible response: Sam felt somewhat shy about his music, but he must have believed in it, otherwise he would not have been able to take Mr. Sargosta's suggestion or put all of his savings into making the recording.

Common Core State Standards

Questions 1–4: Literature 1. Cite textual evidence to support analysis of what the text says explicitly as well as inferences drawn from the text.
Question 5: Literature 3. Describe how a particular story's or drama's plot unfolds in a series of episodes as well as how the characters respond or change as the plot moves toward a resolution.

Name _____

Read the selection. Then answer the questions that follow.

The Impossible Beast

Wildlife experts claim there have been no cougars east of the western states or south | 15
of Canada for decades. They once inhabited much of the eastern United States and are | 30
now "endangered" in North Carolina. | 35

The thing is, I think I saw one this past winter. I was sprucing up an old house I'd | 54
bought at the edge of a Midwestern town, and I wondered about all those huge paw | 70
prints in the snow. They were too big for any canine, but they circled the place as if a | 89
dog had been trying to get inside. | 96

I'd resided here several months when I saw a magnificent animal sauntering through | 109
my ragged meadow into the woods. It was approximately eight or nine feet long from | 124
nose to tail, I estimated, with a back about four feet high. I never saw its head, which | 142
was lowered in the deep grass. Its fur was a golden fawn color, highlighted by the white | 159
sunlight—like photos I've seen of cougars. I still recall the long, powerful tail that | 174
twitched behind the animal's muscular haunches. | 180

In the hardware store I mentioned I'd seen a cougar heading into my woods, and | 195
the news was greeted with compliments to my "vivid imagination." The only cougar | 208
here, a professor who was buying a cordless drill said, was the rock star John Cougar | 224
Mellencamp, who lived nearby, and he'd already dropped his middle name. | 235

I've remained quiet about sightings since then to avoid embarrassment—that is, I did | 249
see it again, prowling through the meadow as before. Once two guests of mine were | 264
walking by the edge of the woods, and a huge wild animal with a long tail sent them | 282
running breathless back to the house. | 288

We all agreed that what we'd seen probably wasn't a cougar, but it sure looked like one. | 305

Turn the page.

Answer the questions below.

1 Most people treated the speaker's claim that he had seen a cougar as a

    A simple mistake.

    (B) sign of his imagination.

    C bid for attention.

    D serious warning.

2 What does the speaker conclude that he saw in his meadow?

    (F) He does not know, but assumes it was not a cougar.

    G He is positive that it was a cougar.

    H He admits that it was just something he imagined.

    J He implies that it was a vision caused by bright sunlight.

3 What details would support the generalization that most people sighting the animal would have thought it was a cougar?

    A North Carolina has declared cougars "endangered."

    B Paw prints too big to be a dog's circled the house.

    (C) The size and fur were like those of a cougar.

    D John Cougar Mellencamp lived nearby.

4 Explain why the speaker became embarrassed to say he'd seen a cougar.

The speaker became embarrassed because no one believed that he'd seen one earlier, and he knew that a cougar in the Midwest was unlikely.

5 In what two areas do most wildlife experts claim that cougars still live?

They live in the western United States and in Canada.

Common Core State Standards

Questions 1, 3, 5: Literature 1. Cite textual evidence to support analysis of what the text says explicitly as well as inferences drawn from the text.
Questions 2, 4: Literature 3. Describe how a particular story's or drama's plot unfolds in a series of episodes as well as how the characters respond or change as the plot moves toward a resolution. **Literature 6.** Explain how an author develops the point of view of the narrator or speaker in a text.

Name _____

Read the selection. Then answer the questions that follow.

What's in a Name?

While playing soccer in the hall, Eddie saw the couple who was moving into 617.	15
The man carried an open box, from which protruded an old hockey stick. The woman	30
followed, carrying a pair of ice skates, a basketball, and a jersey with the name Alex	46
across the back. When she dropped the ball, Eddie ran and picked it up.	60
"Here you go," Eddie said. "So Alex plays hockey? Me too."	71
"Alex will be here tomorrow," the woman volunteered.	79
"You know Alex?" the man asked, squinting inquiringly.	87
"Not yet, but he's into the same stuff I am," Eddie said.	99
The couple smiled knowingly at each other.	106
"So," Eddie said, "how old is Alex?"	113
"Alex is twelve and crazy about soccer and hockey," the woman said. "And	126
basketball." She offered Eddie her hand. "I'm Nonna Aminni, Alex's mother," she said,	139
"and this is Alex's dad, Jonathan."	145
Eddie happened to be in the hall with his soccer ball the next day, a Saturday, when	162
the Aminnis got off the elevator with a girl about his age. She had a long, dark ponytail.	180
She was wearing muddy and rumpled shorts and soccer cleats.	190
"Hi," Eddie gulped.	193
"Eddie," Mrs. Aminni said, "This is Alex."	200
Alex grinned and kicked the ball.	206

Turn the page.

Answer the questions below.

1 **What mistake does Eddie make that most people might have made?**

A   He thinks Alex's parents are the movers.

(B)   He thinks that Alex is a boy.

C   He forgets to hold onto the soccer ball.

D   He thinks that Alex has a sister.

2 **Eddie decides he is eager to meet Alex after he**

(F)   sees hockey equipment in the box.

G   learns that he and Alex are the same age.

H   meets Alex's parents.

J   learns that Alex is a girl.

3 **When do Alex's parents realize that Eddie thinks their daughter is a boy?**

A   They never realize that Eddie thinks that.

B   They see how shocked he is when Alex gets off the elevator.

(C)   They know when Eddie says, "he's into the same stuff I am."

D   They know the minute Eddie asks about when Alex will get there.

4 **How does Eddie know Alex's name before her parents say it?**

He sees the name on the jersey Alex's mother is carrying.

Common Core State Standards

Questions 1–3: Literature 1. Cite textual evidence to support analysis of what the text says explicitly as well as inferences drawn from the text. **Question 4: Literature 3.** Describe how a particular story's or drama's plot unfolds in a series of episodes as well as how the characters respond or change as the plot moves toward a resolution.

Name _____

Read the selection. Then answer the questions that follow.

Laying Claim to Lincoln

Three states claim Abraham Lincoln, our sixteenth President. He was born in 1809	13
in a log cabin in Kentucky, which claims it shaped Lincoln as "the common man."	28
The woman he loved, his best friend, and others of importance to him were all native	44
Kentuckians.	45
The Lincolns moved northward across the Ohio River in 1817, when Abe was seven.	59
He spent his boyhood on a humble Indiana farm that is now a national monument.	74
Abe's Indiana roots included very limited schooling, but he developed an avid attraction	87
to books, which he read by firelight.	94
Abe's mother, Nancy Hanks Lincoln, died when he was ten. Over time, his	107
stepmother, Sarah, became a devoted friend. Indiana claims it fostered Lincoln's	118
determination to learn and his ability to face tragedy.	127
After 1830, the family lived on a farm in Illinois. Abe split rails on the farm and	144
worked as a store clerk, a surveyor, and a postmaster. He studied and practiced law in	160
Springfield and entered politics, serving in the state and U.S. legislatures before losing	173
the race for senator to Stephen Douglas in 1858.	182
Robert Sherwood's 1938 Pulitzer Prize–winning play, *Abe Lincoln in Illinois,* depicts	194
Lincoln as a man struggling with his opposition to slavery and his determination that	208
it would not divide the Union. Lincoln's eloquent speeches opposing slavery were	220
winning national attention, but he said he would preserve the Union even if that meant	235
not freeing the slaves.	239
Lincoln, who was elected President in 1860, did free the slaves. The Civil War began	254
in 1861, and Lincoln led the North to victory, preserving the Union. Re-elected in 1864,	269
he was assassinated in Washington, D.C., shortly after the war ended in 1865.	283
Edwin Stanton, his Secretary of War, said on that day, "Now he belongs to the ages."	299
He truly does—not just to the three states that are so proud to claim him.	315

Turn the page.

Answer the questions below.

1 When did Abraham Lincoln most likely earn the nickname "the rail splitter"?

A when he lived in Kentucky

B while farming in Indiana

(C) after he moved to Illinois

D while serving as President

2 Where was Lincoln living when Sarah Lincoln became part of his life?

F in Kentucky

(G) in Indiana

H in Illinois

J in Washington, D.C.

3 When did Lincoln decide to go into politics?

A before he moved to Indiana

B when his mother died

C after he lost an election to Douglas

(D) after trying other occupations in Illinois

4 What generalization does this selection seem to support?

F Most politicians come from humble beginnings.

(G) A President can be from more than one state.

H In a Civil War, the side the President chooses has an advantage.

J Each state can claim at least one President.

5 What did Stanton mean by "Now he belongs to the ages"?

Lincoln had earned his place in history and would be remembered.

Common Core State Standards

Questions 1–4: Informational Text 1. Cite textual evidence to support analysis of what the text says explicitly as well as inferences drawn from the text.
Question 5: Informational Text 3. Analyze in detail how a key individual, event, or idea is introduced, illustrated, and elaborated in a text (e.g., through examples or anecdotes).

Name _____

Read the selection. Then answer the questions that follow.

The Folks of Stoke

When the *Titanic* sailed for America in April of 1912, the English town | 13

Stoke-on-Trent had just commissioned an artist to sculpt a statue of hometown hero | 26

Edward John Smith. The intention was to honor the magnificent new ship's captain, | 39

who had been at the helm of British passenger liners for more than thirty years. | 54

By the time the statue was completed in 1914, Stoke didn't want it. Then, in 1985, | 70

when the wreckage of the *Titanic* was finally found at the bottom of the Atlantic Ocean, | 86

the people of Stoke changed their minds again. But it was too late. | 99

The "unsinkable" *Titanic* hit an iceberg on April 15, 1912, on its first voyage, and | 114

went under in several hours. It hadn't been Captain Smith's fault that sections of the | 129

double-hulled ship were actually only one layer thick, but eventually many blamed him | 142

for its sinking. The *Titanic* was cruising full speed through a sea he knew was full of | 159

ice. The captain happened not to be at the helm when the gigantic ship collided with an | 176

iceberg, and he was surprisingly cautious responding to the emergency. | 186

Captain Smith knew there weren't enough lifeboats for all the passengers. The crew | 199

realized the ship was sinking, but the captain was reluctant to inform the passengers | 213

with specifics. He commanded, "Stay calm. Be British." | 221

The traditional and valiant captain went down with his ship, and his reputation | 234

sank too. The people of Stoke rejected the finished statue, and the town of Lichfield, | 249

twenty-five miles away, obtained it and placed it in a park. It honors Smith's "great | 264

heart, brave life, and heroic death," and is designated as a national monument. | 277

After the sunken *Titanic* was found, a number of tourists visited Stoke hoping to see | 292

Captain Smith "in the bronze." Stoke wasn't able to get the statue back. Instead tourists | 307

had to be directed to Lichfield. | 313

Turn the page.

Answer the questions below.

1 What made the town of Stoke-on-Trent decide it didn't want the statue of Captain Smith?

A Captain Smith was given command of the *Titanic*.

(B) The *Titanic* sank on its first voyage.

C It was discovered that the *Titanic* didn't have enough lifeboats.

D The statue was designated a national monument.

2 The selection suggests that the *Titanic's* sinking was due to the

F job of captain being given to an inexperienced sailor.

G hometown folks turning their backs on Smith.

H *Titanic* traveling through seas filled with ice.

(J) ship having been made with a single-layered hull.

3 What does the selection suggest led to the town of Stoke-on-Trent wanting the statue after all?

A Captain Smith heroically remained with his ship as it sank.

B The statue was finally completed and ready to be displayed.

C The town of Lichfield wanted it, which made it seem desirable.

(D) The recovered remains of the *Titanic* led to new interest in Smith.

4 What two changes were probably made in ocean liners built after the *Titanic*?

Ocean liners built after the Titanic probably had double-layered hulls. They may have had more lifeboats and fewer passengers.

5 What, according to the selection, did Edward John Smith do that most good captains would probably have done?

Captain Smith stayed with his ship as it sank.

Common Core State Standards

Questions 1–3: Informational Text 1. Cite textual evidence to support analysis of what the text says explicitly as well as inferences drawn from the text.
Questions 4, 5: Informational Text 3. Analyze in detail how a key individual, event, or idea is introduced, illustrated, and elaborated in a text (e.g., through examples or anecdotes).

Read the selection. Then answer the questions that follow.

Letting Them Down Gently

Albert Kolk was flying his grandson and two of the boy's friends up to Canada.	15
Suddenly the plane began spiraling in the dark, "chasing its own tail." Mr. Kolk pulled on	31
a red lever, and a rocket blasted something out of the plane and through a back window!	48
A parachute as big as a house opened above them. It was tied to the plane's nose,	65
wings, and tail; they floated safely to the ground.	74
Back in 2004, the idea of a parachute for a plane was new. Yet more than five	91
hundred small planes had one. Not all of those needed in emergencies had worked, but	106
there were happy endings. One pilot reported that his damaged plane landed so gently	120
in a field under a parachute, some glass ornaments he had on board were not broken.	136
People wondered if larger planes would ever have parachutes. Could parachutes be	148
made huge and strong enough to hold up an airliner's eighty thousand pounds? Would	162
they work at six hundred miles per hour? Would astronauts ever ride in shuttles that had	178
their own parachutes?	181

Turn the page.

Answer the questions below.

1 **How does a plane's parachute get out of the plane and open?**

(A) A rocket blasts it out of the back of the plane.

B It floats out of the plane when it is needed.

C It explodes out of the plane's nose.

D The plane's spiral spins it out into the air.

2 **This selection seems to suggest that this technique could work on most passenger jets if the**

F passengers each had a parachute.

(G) parachutes could be big enough.

H emergencies were not too severe.

J planes were to fly much slower.

3 **What does the selection suggest a plane ride under one of these parachutes would be like?**

A The plane would spiral to the ground.

B It would be like riding a rocket.

(C) It would be a rather gentle, floating ride.

D It would feel like a dog chasing its tail.

4 **At present, does it seem likely that passenger airplanes will soon have parachutes? Use information in the passage to explain your answer.**

No, it does not seem likely. The parachutes on small planes do not work all the time, and there are still more questions than answers about using parachutes for other types of aircraft.

⌐ **Common Core State Standards** ⌐

Questions 1–3: Informational Text 1. Cite textual evidence to support analysis of what the text says explicitly as well as inferences drawn from the text.
Question 4: Informational Text 3. Analyze in detail how a key individual, event, or idea is introduced, illustrated, and elaborated in a text (e.g., through examples or anecdotes).

Name _____

Read the selection. Then answer the questions that follow.

An Opening to Paradise

Just listing the unusual plant and animal life here is like a trip through paradise.	15
These plants and animals are all found in northwest Ohio in the "Oak Openings." The	30
130-square-mile region is "One of America's Last Great Places." It's not a wilderness.	43
Parts of it were once cleared for farming, but its sandy, acidic soil kept most settlers	59
from farming there. So most of it remained undeveloped.	68
Ten thousand years ago, the area was at the southern edge of a great glacial lake. The	85
glacier melted, and the lake drew back, leaving five to fifteen feet of sand to mix with	102
the clay soil. Time left a narrow finger of land, made of dry and acidic soil, on which	120
more than one thousand species of plant life and abundant animal kingdoms flourish.	133
There are a few farms and homes in the area. However, four thousand acres are	148
now conserved as public parks and other public areas. Some people who live in the	163
Openings are cooperating with the government to maintain the ecosystem there.	174
Understandably, such a unique place is an appealing place to live. Developers hope to	188
pack new houses and stores right up against the Openings, and commercial growth will	202
have an impact on and could eliminate the Oak Openings.	212
An effort to protect this precious area while making it accessible so the public can	227
enjoy its incredible variety of plant and animal life never ends. It requires an ongoing	242
awareness campaign. "Stewardship" of Ohio's Oak Openings means educating	251
everyone about its irreplaceable value.	256
Visitors quickly understand how preserved it is when they see the bogs and living	270
sand dunes. When they walk under its pin oak and black oak trees or spot the rare lark	288
sparrow and the spotted turtle or blue-spotted salamander, they realize what a rare	301
treasure this land is. Scarlet tanagers and Karner blue butterflies flit over fields of blue	316
and yellow wildflowers and inspire people to commit to maintaining one of the last	330
great places.	332

Turn the page.

Answer the questions below.

1 Developers would probably argue against the conclusion that

   A everyone would like to live in a modern development.

   B people are more important than butterflies or salamanders.

   C all wild, undeveloped areas should be kept that way.

   D humans are a part of the animal kingdom too.

2 This selection suggests that a geographic region with greatly varied plant life is likely to have

   F many types of birds.

   G few people living near it.

   H careful development and farming.

   J dry and acidic soil.

3 The article notes that the problem of maintaining the Oak Openings is due to the fact that

   A people always want to live near beautiful areas.

   B too much sand can spoil the soil.

   C no one wants to accept stewardship for the region.

   D people are too aware of its great public value.

4 Why did early settlers probably not settle in Oak Openings?

   F The bogs were very dangerous.

   G The sandy soil was bad for farming.

   H It has remained under water until recently.

   J Wildlife frightened most people away.

5 Why might birdwatchers in particular enjoy Oak Openings?

One kind of bird that lives there is rare.

_____

_____

_____

_____

_____

Common Core State Standards

Questions 1–4: Informational Text 1. Cite textual evidence to support analysis of what the text says explicitly as well as inferences drawn from the text.
Question 5: Informational Text 3. Analyze in detail how a key individual, event, or idea is introduced, illustrated, and elaborated in a text (e.g., through examples or anecdotes).

Name _____

Read the selection. Then answer the questions that follow.

A Wide Range of Poets

You might think that the last place to hear poetry would be around a campfire with | 16

cowboys. It turns out that cowboys are as poetic as any folks you can gather. They | 32

sustain poetry as it was invented and intended—as the earliest form of story-telling | 46

and entertainment. Cowboys began reciting poems before there was radio or television. | 58

Many cowboy poems, like ancient ballads, folktales, and American tall tales, were not | 71

written down. | 73

Cowboys are often shown in Western movies as tough, no-nonsense guys who hide | 86

their feelings. Expressing themselves openly in poetry is one of the last things you | 100

would expect from them, but they often like to share their poems. | 112

In 1985 a U.S. agency helped organize the first convention to honor cowboy poetry. | 126

About one hundred cowboy and cowgirl poets from fifteen states gathered and read | 139

their original poems aloud. They also read old favorites they had learned from books | 153

and by listening. Cowpokes have responded enthusiastically ever since. At the Annual | 165

National Cowboy Poets Gathering, there are big shows and dozens of meetings in | 178

different halls. Meanwhile, hundreds of cowboy poetry books have been published, and | 190

numerous Web sites are maintained. There is an international society and a dozen or | 204

more smaller gatherings each year. | 209

What do cowboy poets write about? Well, they tend to be a sentimental bunch, and | 224

many, but not all, of their poems are about their work and their animals. Some even | 240

sing the praises of cows. | 245

It is not unusual to hear a cowboy or cowgirl poet recite something like this: | 260

Riding the range after a day | 266
With the horses and dogs that I love, | 274
I'm thankin' my lucky stars that I may | 282
Sit under that soft light above | 288

And know that the hard day tomorrow will bring— | 297
With its dry, dusty, cold drivin' air— | 304
The challenge to face just any old thing | 312
And breathe deep from the freedom we share. | 320

Turn the page.

Answer the questions below.

1 One reason given that cowboys became poets was that

(A) they had no radio or television for entertainment.

B someone started an annual convention for them.

C poets were needed to appear in Western movies.

D their stories were not being written down.

2 This selection assumes that most people would not consider cowboys to be

F sentimental about wide open spaces.

G interested in gatherings of any kind.

(H) interested in writing poetry.

J proud about the kind of work they do.

3 The selection suggests that often cowboy poetry tends to focus on

A ancient stories.

B radio and television shows.

C what is learned from books.

(D) their work and animals.

4 The poem quoted mentions horses and dogs. What other elements in the poem are probably common in cowboy poetry?

Possible response: Other common elements are probably working outdoors, facing the weather, and the sense of freedom and space.

5 How is much of cowboy poetry similar to the old ballads and tales?

Cowboy poetry, like old ballads and tales, is often shared orally and sometimes is not written down.

Common Core State Standards

Questions 1–3: Informational Text 1. Cite textual evidence to support analysis of what the text says explicitly as well as inferences drawn from the text.
Questions 4, 5: Informational Text 3. Analyze in detail how a key individual, event, or idea is introduced, illustrated, and elaborated in a text (e.g., through examples or anecdotes).

Name _____

Read the selection. Then answer the questions that follow.

A Long Day!

Time is confusing in Spain these days. Working people there follow two very	13
different time schedules. Traditionally, a Spanish workday starts at 9 A.M. and is not	27
over until 8 P.M., with a long break beginning about 2 P.M. and lasting two to three	44
hours.	45
During that break, stores and offices close. People used to go home for naps or	60
siestas, but now most workers take very long, relaxed lunch hours instead. Then it's	74
back to work until 8 P.M., when they go home and sit down to dinner at about 10 P.M.	93
However, many Spaniards are trying to establish work schedules more familiar in	105
the United States—basically from about 8 A.M. until 5 P.M. Parents would like to get	121
home in time to relax with their children, who are home from school, fed, and ready for	138
bed by 8 or 9 P.M.—that is, before people keeping the traditional schedule are home.	154
Confusing? Yes, and it may not be straightened out soon. Tradition tends to prevail in	169
Spain, and many Spaniards aren't ready to think of 8 P.M. as "bedtime."	182

Turn the page.

Answer the questions below.

1 The writer of this selection assumes that the reader will find the traditional Spanish workday

   A appealing.

   B tiring.

   C familiar.

   (D) unusual.

2 Children who have parents following the traditional workday schedule in Spain probably

   F go to schools that run very late as well.

   G don't see much of their parents on workdays.

   (H) eat dinner later.

   J attend schools near the places their parents work.

3 How does the time a traditional Spanish workday starts compare to the time most other people start their days?

   (A) The two kinds of schedules start at around the same time.

   B The traditional workday starts a lot earlier than the other schedule.

   C The traditional workday starts a lot later than the other schedule.

   D The traditional workday starts with a siesta.

4 Explain why workers on the traditional schedule think of 8 P.M. as "afternoon."

They are just finishing their workday, and have yet to go home to enjoy what they consider the evening.

Common Core State Standards

Questions 1–3: Informational Text 1. Cite textual evidence to support analysis of what the text says explicitly as well as inferences drawn from the text.
Question 4: Informational Text 3. Analyze in detail how a key individual, event, or idea is introduced, illustrated, and elaborated in a text (e.g., through examples or anecdotes).

Name _____

Read the selection. Then answer the questions that follow.

A Very Practical Idea

Most towns have something they are known for, and Farmington, known as the	13
home of the University of Maine, is also "the earmuff capital of the world." Years	28
ago, nearly a fourth of all the world's earmuffs were made there. They aren't	42
manufactured in Farmington anymore, but it is the place where earmuffs were	54
invented in 1873, and every year the townspeople there have a parade in December	68
on "Chester Greenwood Day."	72
Chester was fifteen when he invented earmuffs, and he wasn't one of those people	86
who said, "Good idea. I should do something about it." It took Chester two years to	102
get his invention patented, and after that he set up a factory in Farmington to make	118
earmuffs. Being something of an inventor all his life, he invented machines to ensure	132
that the manufacture of Greenwood's Champion Ear Protectors would be consistent and	144
mostly automatic.	146
The idea for earmuffs came to Chester while he was ice skating. He'd tried to	161
protect his sensitive ears by wrapping an itchy scarf around his head. That proved	175
too awkward, so, back home, Chester cut out ear-sized pieces of the scarf and got his	191
grandmother to sew them together to fit over wire loops at the ends of a curved wire	208
that perched on his head.	213
Chester himself went on to invent other things, such as the mechanical mouse trap,	227
shock absorbers for automobiles, the whistling teakettle, and other useful things.	238
Interest in earmuffs eventually waned, though fashion designers have revived it by	250
creating very stylish earmuffs to go with skiing outfits and other winter wear. But	264
fashion earmuffs are not made in Farmington.	271
In the parade on Chester Greenwood Day, you will see earmuffs on everything that	285
moves, including people, animals, and cars. In Maine in winter, it's usually cold enough	299
to demonstrate what a good idea that Farmington teenager had!	309

Turn the page.

Answer the questions below.

1 How do the people of Farmington appear to feel about being "the earmuff capital of the world"?

   A They wish people would forget about Chester Greenwood Day.

   B They regret that there is no earmuff factory there anymore.

   (C) They think it is fun and have a good time with the annual celebration.

   D They wish the world would give Farmington the credit it deserves.

2 What kind of a person does Chester Greenwood seem to have been?

   F He was not nearly as clever as he thought he was.

   (G) He was a bright, creative, and determined boy.

   H He was more interested in selling than in creating things.

   J Once he invented something, he forgot about it.

3 Before Chester Greenwood invented earmuffs, what had to happen?

   A He had to demonstrate that he was a good inventor.

   B A factory to produce what he invented had to be found.

   C His state had to recognize how talented he was.

   (D) He had to be out in the cold with his sensitive ears.

4 Why do the people of Farmington and Maine hold an annual parade in honor of earmuffs?

   (F) Chester Greenwood helped make their town and state special.

   G They are hoping someone will get the earmuff factory going again.

   H They feel they must prove where earmuffs were invented.

   J Other inventors need that encouragement to do their best work.

5 When an invention is created, what is the intent of the inventor, and who benefits from a successful invention?

An inventor is usually trying to solve his or her own problem when he or she invents something, and a successful invention benefits the inventor and many other people, making their lives easier and more comfortable.

Common Core State Standards

Questions 1–4: Informational Text 1. Cite textual evidence to support analysis of what the text says explicitly as well as inferences drawn from the text.
Question 5: Informational Text 3. Analyze in detail how a key individual, event, or idea is introduced, illustrated, and elaborated in a text (e.g., through examples or anecdotes).

Name _____

Read the selection. Then answer the questions that follow.

Fearing Extinction

In April of 1999, after hunting turkeys in the Pearl River Wildlife Management Area | 14
in southeastern Louisiana, college student David Kulivan came out of the forest and | 27
reported watching something unusual at close range for a quarter of an hour. His report | 42
excited naturalists across the nation! | 47

Soon planes were scouting the huge forest area to begin plans for a scientific, | 61
intensive search. It took over a year to enlist the best experts for the expedition. | 76
They would venture into deep bayous and flooded forest bottoms, carrying cameras, | 88
recorders, and computers. | 91

Meanwhile, people were discussing David and his report. He did not seem to be | 105
staging a hoax, but was he just hopeful and merely believing what he wanted to see? | 121

This excursion was not the first dedicated attempt to observe the ivory-billed | 133
woodpecker, and no one had yet been successful. It had been more than fifty years | 148
since a credible sighting of this, the largest of the woodpeckers, even though claims | 162
of sightings had been made approximately every decade, giving people hope that the | 175
ivory-billed was not, as most feared, extinct. | 182

Reported sightings of the ivory-billed are usually assumed to be sightings of the | 195
pileated woodpecker, a beautiful large woodpecker that is similar to, but smaller than, | 208
the ivory-billed. Many pileated woodpeckers inhabit areas of the United States. They | 220
are, like the ivory-billed, a combination of black and white. | 230

Both the male and female pileated woodpeckers have dramatic red crests, while only | 243
the ivory-billed male has one. There are other distinctions. The ivory-billed has a longer | 257
whitish bill, which explains its name. There are also differences in the "chin" and other | 272
markings, which David Kulivan knew and noted when describing what he saw. | 284

The excursion in 2002 did not confirm that the ivory-billed is not extinct. Still, most | 299
people believe—want to believe—that David's report was a credible sighting of this | 313
mysterious, elusive bird. | 316

Turn the page.

Answer the questions below.

1 The details in the second paragraph suggest that when experts do scientific studies they

   A need to ask for permission.

   B need to spend a year in college.

   C need to make claims of sightings before venturing on location.

   (D) need to go to the location equipped with necessary tools.

2 The selection makes it clear that

   F there have been many credible sightings of the ivory-billed woodpecker in the last fifty years.

   (G) the excursion could not confirm the sighting.

   H Kulivan's sighting of the ivory-billed woodpecker was a hoax.

   J the ivory-billed woodpecker is extinct.

3 The details in paragraphs 5 and 6 lead us to conclude that the ivory-billed woodpecker and the pileated woodpecker

   (A) are different in many ways.

   B live in areas outside the United States.

   C are the same size and colors.

   D have long, whitish bills.

4 Why did Kulivan's report raise more interest than other reports in the last fifty years?

Kulivan's sighting seemed credible because he watched the woodpecker for a quarter of an hour and noted a lot of details about its appearance, all of which matched the characteristics of the ivory-billed woodpecker.

5 Based on the selection and its title, what can we conclude about all the reported sightings of the ivory-billed woodpecker?

People who make such reports are usually mistaken, but enthusiasts and naturalists still hope to prove that the ivory-billed woodpecker is not extinct.

Common Core State Standards

Questions 1–3: Informational Text 1. Cite textual evidence to support analysis of what the text says explicitly as well as inferences drawn from the text.
Questions 4, 5: Informational Text 3. Analyze in detail how a key individual, event, or idea is introduced, illustrated, and elaborated in a text (e.g., through examples or anecdotes).

Name _____

Read the selection. Then answer the questions that follow.

Disposable Phones

In 1999, toy maker Randi Altschul was driving and talking on her cell phone. The	15
voice at the other end began to crackle and fade. She longed to toss her cell phone in	33
the garbage, but a cell phone is expensive. Suddenly, an idea occurred to her: a cheap,	49
disposable cell phone. Technologists built a very thin model out of recyclable plastic	62
for Altschul's company, Dieceland. The phone was about three times as thick as a credit	77
card and folded in thirds. Inside the plastic coiled a long, twisting circuit.	90
By 2002, other companies had announced plans to build a disposable cell phone.	103
However, trouble with design, keeping costs down, and getting approval from the	115
Federal Communications Commission put most companies out of the race. In 2008,	127
Hop-On Communications announced that the first disposable cell phone was ready to	139
be sold. Its cost? Ten dollars. The HOP1800 has no display, so you can't see who's	155
calling or the number you've dialed. The wait for a disposable cell phone people will	170
buy may not be over!	175

Turn the page.

- -

Answer the questions below.

1 **What is the main idea of this selection?**

  A Plastic is the most popular material for phones.

  B Developing ideas into products is simple.

  C Ideas for new products can come from anyone.

  (D) The solution to a problem can be a new product.

2 **Suppose that in 1999 Altschul had used a HOP1800 phone. What would she *most likely* do if her connection failed again?**

  F purchase a more expensive phone

  (G) throw the phone into the nearest garbage can

  H stop and place the phone call again

  J invent improved cell phone networks

3 **Based on the selection, for what reason may people decide *against* buying the HOP1800 phone?**

  A They would rather get cell phones that are disposable.

  (B) They prefer to see the phone numbers displayed.

  C They believe phone companies raced to reduce costs.

  D They think Altschul's phone has a better design.

4 **Why would choosing the right type of plastic be important for designing a disposable cell phone? Explain your answer.**

Possible response: It is likely that disposable phones would just get thrown away. You need to be able to recycle them. Plastics and materials that are not recyclable would end up in a landfill and be bad for the environment.

Common Core State Standards

Question 1: Informational Text 2. Determine a central idea of a text and how it is conveyed through particular details; provide a summary of the text distinct from personal opinions or judgments. **Questions 2–4: Informational Text 1.** Cite textual evidence to support analysis of what the text says explicitly as well as inferences drawn from the text.

Name _____

Read the selection. Then answer the questions that follow.

Where Ideas Come From

Have you ever wondered where ideas for inventions come from? Inventors don't	12
always come up with their ideas alone. Sometimes ideas bloom from a conversation	25
with someone else. This happened to Thomas Adams in 1869.	35
Adams had been a photographer, but he was trying to become an inventor. General	49
Santa Anna, the former, overthrown president of Mexico, was visiting Adams's house	61
on Staten Island, New York, after fleeing his own country. He knew that Adams wanted	76
to be an inventor so he offered a suggestion. He suggested Adams use a rubbery	91
Mexican substance called *chicle* to make rubber tires. Santa Anna had brought a lot of	106
chicle with him to America, hoping to make a profit using it in carriage tires, but that	123
had not worked out. Adams liked Santa Anna's suggestion, and he began to experiment.	137
Alas, his tire experiments failed too. Then he tried to make chicle toys and rain boots.	153
Those attempts also failed. Thomas was frustrated. He wanted to use the chicle in a	168
new item, but he didn't have any fresh ideas.	177
Adams finally recalled that Santa Anna often chewed chicle for pleasure. Adams had	190
never tried that. He popped a piece of chicle into his mouth, and began to chew.	206
Elsewhere in the United States, chewing gum was also in the making. The Fleer	220
brothers used an extract from the Sapodilla tree, covering it with a hard white	234
coating. They did not market the gum widely, though. The Curtis brothers in Maine	248
experimented with spruce tree resin, switching to paraffin later. Adams experimented	259
with putting licorice in the chicle gum and manufactured the first flavored chewing	272
gum in the United States. It was called "Black Jack" and came in the shape of a stick.	290
People loved it, and Adams was officially an inventor.	299

Turn the page.

Answer the questions below.

1 The main idea of this selection is

    A chewing gum has been around for many years.

    B an inventor has to be smart.

    (C) great ideas of inventors can be inspired by others.

    D all chewing gum is made from *chicle*.

2 Santa Anna most likely gave Adams the suggestion to use *chicle* to make tires because as an inventor Adams seemed

    F unable to create ideas.

    G distracted.

    H on the wrong track.

    (J) open to input from others.

3 Why was Adams's gum probably more successful than that of the Fleer or Curtis brothers?

    (A) Flavoring the gum made it more pleasing to chew.

    B The Curtis brothers used paraffin.

    C The Fleer brothers were bad at marketing.

    D Gum that came in chunks was less marketable.

4 Based on what the selection tells you about Adams, what do you think inventors *must not do* in order to succeed?

    F remain open to suggestions

    G learn from their failures

    (H) give up on a project idea

    J work hard every day

5 What was General Santa Anna's role in Adams's success?

Possible response: General Santa Anna had chicle, and he suggested it to Adams as something to experiment with.

Common Core State Standards

Question 1: Informational Text 2. Determine a central idea of a text and how it is conveyed through particular details; provide a summary of the text distinct from personal opinions or judgments. **Questions 2–4: Informational Text 1.** Cite textual evidence to support analysis of what the text says explicitly as well as inferences drawn from the text. **Question 5: Informational Text 3.** Analyze in detail how a key individual, event, or idea is introduced, illustrated, and elaborated in a text (e.g., through examples or anecdotes).

Read the selection. Then answer the questions that follow.

In the Hive

Early beehives were simply shelters shaped like boxes or "hives." As beekeepers | 12

learned about bee colonies' needs and the interior layout of a hive, hive structures | 26

were modernized to make gathering honey safer for the interior architecture of the | 39

hive. For example, there is one queen, and she stays in a "brood nest" where she lays | 56

all of her eggs. The nest is in a safe location. This was at the center of the early hives, | 76

and the drone (worker) bees built "honeycombs" along the sides. In later hives, bars | 90

were stretched over the open top. The bars and the attached, dangling combs could be | 105

lifted out without disturbing the brood nest below. Modern hives are boxes that have | 119

removable trays. The tray structure allows the beekeeper to check on the health of the | 134

bees and gather honey without disturbing the business of the hive. It also allows the | 149

beekeeper to start a new hive without greatly disrupting the previous one. | 161

One basic goal of the beekeeper is to keep the bees calm. The beekeeper aims to | 177

provide a safe and productive environment for the bees to live in and make honey. | 192

When working with a colony, beekeepers do not wear dark, rough, or woolly fabric | 206

or perfume or lotion. Those fabrics and unusual odors alarm the bees and can induce | 221

"swarming behavior." Swarming behavior occurs when the odor of bee venom excites | 233

other bees to sting; a mass of bees excite themselves into a frenzy. Beekeepers do | 248

occasionally experience stings when handling the colony. One way they can protect | 260

themselves is by wearing a veil over the face and head or even a full beekeeping suit, a | 278

puffy white outfit that makes the beekeeper look like an astronaut. | 289

Turn the page.

Answer the questions below.

1 "In the Hive" is mainly about
(A) hives and beekeepers.
B the behavior of drone bees.
C ways beekeepers avoid being stung.
D the production of honey.

2 The structure of hives was changed to
F keep bees from swarming.
G protect the bees from weather.
H keep the bees enclosed in the hive.
(J) allow for the safe gathering of honey.

3 The biggest problem with early hives was that
A the brood nest was too close to the sides.
B beekeepers got stung reaching in.
(C) the hive's architecture was easily damaged.
D the hives could not be easily moved.

4 Why do you think bees become agitated when they smell bee venom?

They know that a threat must be near if one or more members of the hive used their stingers and emitted venom.

5 Do you think a good beekeeper would be more likely to check a hive daily or weekly? Explain your answer.

Answers may vary. A good beekeeper would be more likely to check a hive weekly because the goal is not to disturb the bees any more than is necessary.

6 Copyright © Pearson Education, Inc., or its affiliates. All Rights Reserved.

Common Core State Standards

Question 1: Informational Text 2. Determine a central idea of a text and how it is conveyed through particular details; provide a summary of the text distinct from personal opinions or judgments. **Questions 2, 3: Informational Text 1.** Cite textual evidence to support analysis of what the text says explicitly as well as inferences drawn from the text. **Questions 4, 5: Informational Text 3.** Analyze in detail how a key individual, event, or idea is introduced, illustrated, and elaborated in a text (e.g., through examples or anecdotes).

Name _____

Read the selection. Then answer the questions that follow.

Can Cats Think?

Most people agree that cats are intelligent animals. Some cats appear to be more	14
intelligent than others. But many people insist that all cats behave as if they are	29
thinking things through.	32
Certain cat behaviors suggest that cats are thinking. By nature, cats are cautious and	46
able to sense when a threat is nearby. They are also very curious. They love to explore	63
new environments and locations. They will nap in half-open drawers, in empty grocery	76
sacks, or on a sweater on a chair. Finally, cats can solve problems. If a cat is cold, he	95
will sit under a lamp. If he wants to catch a squirrel, he will wait under a tree. Most	114
cats that live with people are smart enough to get the people to open the door for them.	132
They go outside to roam and come back in whenever they want.	144

Turn the page.

Answer the questions below.

1 Why do you think the author wrote "Can Cats Think?"

   A to tell funny facts about cats

   (B) to persuade you that cats have thoughts

   C to instruct the reader how to train cats

   D to show how living with people changes cats

2 The author writes, "Some cats appear to be more intelligent than others." Which words tell the reader that this is an opinion?

   F some cats

   (G) appear to be

   H more intelligent

   J than others

3 The tone of the author of the selection can best be described as

   A serious.

   B funny.

   C scientific.

   (D) friendly.

4 Do you think the author wanted to persuade readers to adopt cats as pets? Why or why not?

Answers may vary. Possible response: I don't think so. Even though the author described cats as smart animals and so probably thinks cats make good pets, the author was mostly trying to persuade you that cats were brainy. There were not any reasons why it would be a good idea to have one live with you.

Common Core State Standards

Questions 1–4: Informational Text 6. Determine an author's point of view or purpose in a text and explain how it is conveyed in the text.

Name _____

Read the selection. Then answer the questions that follow.

Kenaf: The Wonder Plant

Kenaf (ka NEF) is indeed a wonder plant. It is an ancient crop grown in Africa for	17
four thousand years. The Egyptians used it as food for their animals. A member of the	33
cotton family, kenaf will grow anywhere cotton grows, and it grows extremely rapidly.	46
In about five months when it is ready for harvest, the plant is twelve to fourteen feet	63
tall. In the southern United States, where the winter is not too cold, kenaf farmers often	79
have two growing seasons at the same time farmers of other crops have one. Both the	95
inside and the outside of the tall cane-like stalk can be made into different products.	110
Kenaf has been in the United States since the mid-1950s. Several government	122
agencies and universities have studied kenaf for many years. Research reveals that this	135
single plant has a variety of uses. The many products that can be made from kenaf	151
include cooking oil, bedding for horses, food for cattle, cat litter, fabric, and paper.	165
This hardy plant is truly remarkable. It can be made into many different items whose	180
quality is superior to other materials. For example, kenaf paper is stronger than paper	194
made from southern pine trees. It also costs less to make, and the process is easier	210
on the environment. One government study states that for the same number of acres	224
planted in kenaf and in pine trees, kenaf produces about four times more fiber than	239
pine trees. Also, it takes from seven to forty years for pines to grow tall enough to be	257
harvested. Kenaf can be harvested in only five months.	266

Turn the page.

Answer the questions below.

1 Based on the information in the selection, which is most likely true of the author?

A The author grows kenaf for profit.

(B) The author thinks kenaf is a valuable crop.

C The author thinks kenaf is the grain of the future.

D The author wants readers to buy kenaf products.

2 Which of these best supports the title of the selection?

F Kenaf will grow anywhere cotton grows.

G Kenaf has been in the United States since the mid-1950s.

(H) Research reveals that this single plant has a variety of uses.

J It takes seven to forty years for pines to grow tall enough to be harvested.

3 What does the author use to convince readers about kenaf's value?

A humorous sayings

(B) factual information

C personal stories

D historical records

4 The author wrote, "This hardy plant is truly remarkable." Which of the following states the same opinion?

F Kenaf can be harvested in only five months.

G Several government agencies have studied kenaf.

H Kenaf is a member of the cotton family.

(J) Kenaf is indeed a wonder plant.

5 Did the author persuade you that kenaf paper is better than pine paper? Explain.

Answers may vary. Students should support their answers with reasons from the passage.

Common Core State Standards

Questions 1–5: Informational Text 6. Determine an author's point of view or purpose in a text and explain how it is conveyed in the text.

Name _____

Read the selection. Then answer the questions that follow.

Bats: An Asset

Many people think of bats as blind, daring creatures that swoop out of nowhere at	15
night, making an odd screeching noise and aiming at a person's hair or neck. None of	34
this is true. The bat's reputation as a scary Halloween creature is undeserved. Bats are	46
useful, peaceful animals that would probably prefer not to encounter people at all.	59
Bats fly at night, locating things by a "sonar" system. That is, they sense the sound	75
waves from living and non-living things. They're out primarily to hunt insects, the	88
main part of their diet. In fact, bats improve the environmental conditions for people	102
by devouring insects such as mosquitoes. A colony of only 150 large brown bats can	117
gobble almost thirty-three million rootworms in a summer, giving crops the protection	129
necessary for a good harvest. A Mexican colony of twenty million free-tailed bats	142
typically eats two hundred tons of insects every night. Bats are also a source of	157
pollination and spreading of seeds for plants such as bananas, dates, and figs. Clearly,	171
bats are an asset rather than a threat.	179
Bat conservationists, concerned about different bat species becoming extinct,	188
popularized "bat houses" in the United States in the 1980s. Over time, they discovered	202
that bats prefer to roost a quarter mile or less from a stream, river, or large lake and	220
to be near orchards, fields used to grow crops, or the woods. The best-liked houses	235
were stained dark and placed in a location that got at least four hours of sun per day.	253
One study showed that the higher up a bat house is placed, the more likely it is to	271
be occupied. Bats clearly prefer to keep their distance from people and to socialize	285
amongst themselves.	287

Turn the page.

Answer the questions below.

1 Which of the following best describes the author's argument about bats?

   A Bats must be kept in bat houses away from people.

   B Bats are tame enough that people could pet them.

   (C) Bats are harmless and helpful to people.

   D Houses should be provided for all bats in the United States.

2 Why did the author most likely discuss what some species of bats eat?

   F to show that bats do not eat meat

   G to avoid saying what other species of bats eat

   H to explain why bats fly only at night

   (J) to imply what a large number of insects the bats eat

3 Based on the selection, which of the following is a statement of opinion?

   A Bats fly at night, guided by sound waves.

   (B) Bats are an asset, not a threat.

   C The most successful bat houses are set high.

   D Bats prefer to live near fresh water.

4 Does the author appear to think that bat houses are a good idea? Why or why not?

Possible response: The author appears to think that bat houses are a good idea. The author describes what makes a bat house attractive to bats, implying that it is worth building more houses like these.

5 Bat conservationists apparently persuaded many people to build bat houses. Based on the selection, describe the people *most likely* to agree to build one.

Possible response: Since bats seem to eat so many insects, people having trouble with bugs outdoors could want bats around. People who have yards and trees and who are concerned about the environment might build bat houses, especially if they live near water or have vegetable gardens.

Common Core State Standards

Questions 1–5: Informational Text 6. Determine an author's point of view or purpose in a text and explain how it is conveyed in the text.

Name _____

Read the selection. Then answer the questions that follow.

Mighty Joe Bob and Jack

Mighty Joe Bob is a distinguished character, bigger than life, who roamed the Texas	14
Hill Country in years gone by. Nobody ever actually saw Mighty Joe Bob, but every	29
rancher around knows who he was and what he and his dog, Jack, did. They know that	46
Mighty Joe Bob was responsible for bringing river water to the Hill Country.	59
A long time ago there was no natural water in the hills. The whole area was parched	76
under the blistering sun until Mighty Joe Bob gave Jack a bone. Jack gnawed his bone	92
for three days, but ate only a third of it. When Jack dug a hole to bury the rest, he	112
struck a pool of underground water. Freezing cold water bubbled from the ground and	126
flowed freely.	128
So today, there is cold, clean water snaking through the Hill Country.	140

Turn the page.

Answer the questions below.

1 The author's statement that nobody ever saw Mighty Joe Bob most likely suggests that

(A) Mighty Joe Bob might be a myth.

B Mighty Joe Bob was good at hiding from people.

C some people lied about having seen him.

D Jack's owner was someone else.

2 Because Jack dug a hole for his bone,

F ranchers know where to find bones.

G he was able to save two-thirds of it for a later time.

(H) water sprang from the ground.

J the bone polluted the water.

3 Because every rancher seemed to know the story of Mighty Joe Bob and Jack, you can assume that

(A) ranchers all passed the story around.

B ranchers all used the water.

C ranchers built dams to contain the water.

D ranchers appreciate what Mighty Joe Bob and Jack did.

4 Why do you think there was no natural water in the Hill Country until Jack dug the hole?

Answers may vary. Possible response: No one had thought to dig below the surface for an underground spring.

Common Core State Standards

Questions 1–4: Literature 1. Cite textual evidence to support analysis of what the text says explicitly as well as inferences drawn from the text.

Read the selection. Then answer the questions that follow.

Franco's Choice

Franco awoke as usual, got dressed, and headed for school like he always did. While | 15

riding his bicycle, he thought about how routine everything was. | 25

Three blocks from school, Franco stopped at the corner realizing he had a choice. He | 40

could go straight as always, or he could turn left and take the longer path to school. He | 58

needed some variety, so Franco turned left. | 65

Franco noticed a white automobile speeding toward the school, and he thought the | 78

driver ought to slow down. Unexpectedly, he saw something that made him skid to a | 93

stop. He saw an object soar from the car window and land in the tall weeds near the | 111

sidewalk. He sped to the site where the object had landed. There, Franco scoured the | 126

weeds until he found a man's billfold, and thought it might have been stolen. Thanks to | 142

police shows on TV, he knew he shouldn't touch anything that was stolen, so he used | 158

his lunch bag to pick up the billfold. Franco then rushed to school. He marched into the | 175

office and turned in the billfold. | 181

Later, Mr. Jones, the principal, found Franco in the lunchroom eating his sandwich. | 194

"May I have your attention?" he shouted above the lunchroom noise. Everyone grew | 207

quiet. "I want to tell you about Franco," Mr. Jones said. Franco choked on his tuna | 223

sandwich. "Franco found a billfold and brought it to the office. We called the police | 238

and learned the billfold had been stolen. Thank you, Franco, for being a model citizen. | 253

And here is a fifty dollar reward from the billfold's owner. Let's all give Franco a | 269

big hand." The lunchroom rocked with thunderous applause. Mr. Jones was proud of | 282

Franco, and Franco felt proud too. | 288

Turn the page.

Answer the questions below.

1 Based on the reaction of Mr. Jones and others in the lunchroom, Franco will probably be known as a

A bicyclist.

B fool.

C hero.

D tattletale.

2 Franco probably rushed to find the billfold in the weeds because he was

F curious.

G worried.

H confident.

J scared.

3 Why do you think the author wrote this story?

A to persuade the reader to change daily routines

B to inform the reader of ways to get a reward

C to express concern over crime

D to inform the reader of the importance of our choices

4 Because Franco took a different way to school, he

F decided always to use that route.

G had an unexpected experience.

H was late to school.

J got to meet Mr. Jones.

5 The title of the story is "Franco's Choice." What do you think Franco learned from his choice?

Answers may vary. Possible response: There are rewards for making the right and honest choice.

Common Core State Standards

Questions 1–4: Literature 1. Cite textual evidence to support analysis of what the text says explicitly as well as inferences drawn from the text. **Question 5: Literature 3.** Describe how a particular story's or drama's plot unfolds in a series of episodes as well as how the characters respond or change as the plot moves toward a resolution.

Name _____

Read the selection. Then answer the questions that follow.

The Girl in the Maroon Robe

During the sixth grade, I constantly wore a maroon flannel robe. In fact, I wore it | 16

so often it literally shredded one day in the washing machine. It wasn't particularly | 30

attractive; it didn't even have pockets, but I loved it. It was comfortable and made me | 46

feel secure. | 48

Feeling secure was vital because I had low self-esteem. I was taller than all the boys, | 64

skinny as a rail, and clumsy too. I was forever running into desks, causing enormous | 79

bruises on my body. One day, I brought a chocolate cake to school for Coach Marshall | 95

on Teacher Appreciation Day, but before I could deliver it, I accidentally dropped the | 109

cake upside down in the hall. Everyone laughed, even those who tried not to. | 123

That was my sixth grade existence. I could accomplish nothing worthwhile. Then | 135

one weekend day Mrs. Powers, a neighbor, stopped me at our mailbox. I was enveloped | 150

in my maroon robe. She admitted she was concerned about me because I looked so | 165

miserable. I wailed and explained how I felt. I felt hideous, and that I couldn't do | 181

anything right. Mrs. Powers touched me on the shoulder. It felt like an angel's hand | 196

rested there. Mrs. Powers said, "Laurie, you're a diamond in the rough. One day you | 211

will shine brilliantly. Don't worry." Often remembering her words, I've cherished them | 223

for decades. | 225

I presume she recognized the value in me that I was too blind to see. Her thoughtful | 242

words made me feel authentic, and I started thinking of myself as a diamond— | 256

beautiful, strong, and shining. | 260

As an award-winning writer today, I outshine my competition in every article I pen, | 274

and I refuse to wear a flannel robe. | 282

Turn the page.

Answer the questions below.

1 What event caused a positive change for the author?
- **A** entering the seventh grade
- **B** getting a maroon robe
- **(C)** Mrs. Powers's expression of concern
- **D** making a chocolate cake for Coach Marshall

2 The author refuses to wear a flannel robe today because
- **F** she has a silk one.
- **(G)** her writing success makes her feel secure.
- **H** her maroon robe was destroyed in the wash.
- **J** it can't replace her favorite one.

3 Based on the selection, what might be beneficial to all sixth graders?
- **(A)** having an adult believe in them
- **B** trying to stand out in the crowd
- **C** taking a cake to school
- **D** owning flannel robes

4 Why do you think the author wrote about her sixth-grade experience?

Answers may vary. Possible response: The author wanted to express hope to sixth graders who feel the same way and who might also be ready to discover their own strengths.

5 The author became an award-winning writer. What else does using her talent appear to have done for her?

Answers may vary. Possible response: Her talent for writing made her feel confident in her abilities in other aspects of her life.

Common Core State Standards

Questions 1–4: **Literature 1.** Cite textual evidence to support analysis of what the text says explicitly as well as inferences drawn from the text. **Question 5:** **Literature 3.** Describe how a particular story's or drama's plot unfolds in a series of episodes as well as how the characters respond or change as the plot moves toward a resolution.

Name _____

Read the selection. Then answer the questions that follow.

Let's Get This Right

Gina showed up for school complaining to her friend Laura Mae about how	13
hectic things had been at her house the previous night. "I couldn't get the geography	28
assignment completed for Mrs. Lightner," she said, "so you've got to let me copy what	43
you did."	45
"Sorry," Laura Mae said, "I won't do that." Laura Mae's simple rule about cheating	59
was that she simply didn't do it.	66
"Look," Gina said, "either you help me out this one time, or we're no longer	81
friends."	82
Shocked by Gina's threat, Laura Mae stood silently by the school entrance, thinking	95
hard. She and Gina had been best friends for three years. "Let's discuss this with	110
Mrs. Lightner," she said. "I know she'll let you have another day if we explain, and I	127
promise to help you complete the work tonight."	135
Gina shook her head. It was *either/or*, she repeated. Either Laura Mae helped, or the	150
friendship was over.	154
"You're drawing the wrong conclusion," Laura Mae said with a frown. "This is an	168
if/then situation. If I let you bully me into cheating, then our friendship is over for	185
certain."	186

Turn the page.

Answer the questions below.

1 The "if/then" situation Laura Mae proposed tried to persuade
   - (A) Gina to make a choice between two things.
   - **B** Mrs. Lightner to go easy on Gina.
   - **C** someone to organize things at Gina's house.
   - **D** Gina to help her later with a future assignment.

2 How did Laura Mae respond to Gina's threat?
   - **F** She reported her to Mrs. Lightner.
   - **G** She let Gina copy her homework.
   - **H** She said their friendship was over.
   - (J) She suggested a different solution.

3 Which sentence is the *best* summary of this story's plot?
   - **A** A girl refuses to help a friend complete her homework.
   - **B** A girl asks a friend to help her cheat on homework.
   - (C) A friendship is tested by a disagreement about cheating.
   - **D** A friendship ends because a girl completed her homework.

4 What or who does Gina seem to consider responsible for her not completing the geography assignment?

   Gina blames the hectic situation at her house the night

   before.

Common Core State Standards

Questions 1, 2: Literature 1. Cite textual evidence to support analysis of what the text says explicitly as well as inferences drawn from the text.
Question 3: Literature 2. Determine a theme or central idea of a text and how it is conveyed through particular details; provide a summary of the text distinct from personal opinions or judgments. **Question 4: Literature 3.** Describe how a particular story's or drama's plot unfolds in a series of episodes as well as how the characters respond or change as the plot moves toward a resolution.

Name _____

Read the selection. Then answer the questions that follow.

Looking Out for Lady

Marshall fed his dog Lady "Garden," a dog food advertised on TV as containing	14
vegetables. One day he looked on the bag and realized there were practically none in	29
the product.	32
The next day at the pet mall, Marshall and Lady strolled along the aisles of dry	48
food. He leaned over bags of a brand name he recognized and ran his finger across	64
the information on it. A clerk wearing a green apron with "Primo" embroidered on it	79
explained, "Almost all of a food's content is covered by the first four ingredients listed,	94
and that product lists corn third under its ingredients."	103
"I like corn," Marshall acknowledged.	108
"Corn's difficult for dogs to digest," the man said, "so they don't get as much	123
nutrition from it as from a formula with rice. Corn's inexpensive to include and it	138
crowds out better ingredients."	142
"What do you recommend?" Marshall asked.	148
The man pointed at the name "Primo" on his apron. "No yellow corn in 'Primo,'" he	164
said, "and no animal by-products."	169
"Animal by-products sound unappetizing," Marshall agreed.	175
"They're food, but they don't provide a high-quality protein, while Primo Lamb	187
and Rice has the best ingredients you can feed this girl," he said, stooping to pet Lady.	204
The man added that Primo contained glucosamine and chondroitin "for healthy joints"	216
and that other ingredients would protect Lady's heart and maintain her glossy coat. He	230
pointed to each ingredient on a bag of Primo, which included, he claimed, more of the	246
healthful ingredients than other brands.	251
"How long have you worked for the store?" Marshall asked.	261
"I don't work for the store. I represent Primo," the man said.	273
Marshall became suspicious of the advice he was getting. He spent a half hour	287
comparing the ingredients of different dog food.	294
"There's a special now on Primo Lamb and Rice," the man said, passing by again.	309
"Each bag contains ten extra pounds, free."	316
Marshall acted like he faced a tough decision, then said, "I guess I'll try one	331
of those."	333

Turn the page.

Answer the questions below.

1 **What has the salesman concluded about corn?**

A Dogs like corn more than other vegetables.

B Corn provides better nutrition for dogs than rice does.

(C) Some companies use corn because it is inexpensive.

D Very little corn is used in most dog food.

2 **What is the problem that Marshall faces in this story?**

F His dog's dry food contains too few vegetables.

G He thinks the clerk is not being truthful with him.

H He must determine the best sale price for Primo.

(J) He wants to find the healthiest brand of dog food.

3 **The salesman wants Marshall to conclude that Primo Lamb and Rice**

A is a lot like most other dog food.

B contains a lot of corn.

(C) is better than all other dog food.

D contains a lot of vegetables.

4 **What does Marshall conclude about the man in the green apron?**

(F) He just wants to sell Marshall some Primo dog food.

G He wants Marshall to have the best for Lady.

H He actually works for the store.

J He doesn't know much about dog food.

5 **Why does Marshall decide to buy Primo?**

Possible response: Reading the dog food bags has not shown one brand to be superior, and the free ten pounds with a Primo purchase makes up his mind.

Common Core State Standards

Questions 1–4: Literature 1. Cite textual evidence to support analysis of what the text says explicitly as well as inferences drawn from the text. **Question 5: Literature 3.** Describe how a particular story's or drama's plot unfolds in a series of episodes as well as how the characters respond or change as the plot moves toward a resolution.

Name _____

Read the selection. Then answer the questions that follow.

A Temporary Solution

Diego's Uncle Lucas gave odd birthday gifts. Sometimes, though, Diego thought	11
they were really cool. For example, the time when Diego got a little portable CD player	27
with earphones made him think his Uncle Lucas was better than Santa Claus. However,	41
he was less enthusiastic the year he got a finger monitor to test his blood pressure.	57
The story was that Uncle Lucas had once edited some kind of catalog for a big store	74
chain and then later for an Internet warehouse. We assumed that product distributors	87
had given those things to Lucas as gifts. When a holiday or birthday came along, he	103
wrapped one up, unused, and gave it as a gift.	113
The rule was never to reveal your disappointment if you got something peculiar and	127
to act grateful, even as if you had requested it. That worked tolerably well until Diego	143
unwrapped the label maker. It was fun at first. Diego typed in the name of something	159
and then stuck it on the object. "Notebook," Diego's notebook read.	170
Diego seemed very satisfied by naming things so plainly. Then he got carried away	184
and assumed the label maker would guarantee him an exceptionally well-organized life.	196
Labeling stuff became his obsession, and everything he owned, he said, was going to	210
have a label. You get a label maker from your kind uncle, and you put your life in order.	229
"Stop, please!" I cried one afternoon as Diego labeled pieces of chalk with their	243
colors. He looked at me, realizing how ridiculous it all was. His face crinkled up, and he	260
started punching the keypad on that contraption like mad. Out came a long piece of tape	276
that Diego peeled and stuck across my shoulder. It read, "My helpful *amigo* Carlos."	290
I was about to object when I noticed that the first labels Diego had put on things	307
were starting to peel off. The threat of the useful label maker would not last long.	323

Turn the page.

Answer the questions below.

1 According to the story, how did people believe Uncle Lucas selected the strange gifts he gave?

   A shopping in unusual catalogs

   B buying gifts on the Internet

   (C) choosing among free gifts he'd gotten

   D basing them on things people had requested

2 According to the speaker, Diego assumed that labeling all his things would help him

   F get work as a catalog editor.

   (G) put his things in good order.

   H show people how many things he had.

   J tell Uncle Lucas what kinds of things he needed.

3 What conclusion did Diego draw that the speaker disagreed with?

   A Uncle Lucas was a terrible shopper.

   (B) The label maker was a useful tool.

   C Uncle Lucas did not buy the gifts himself.

   D It was a good idea to act as if the gifts pleased you.

4 How is labeling the colored chalk the climax of the things Diego labeled?

The examples of what Diego labeled became more and more silly, and labeling the colored chalk made him realize just how much. Putting a label on Carlos is Diego's way of acknowledging that.

5 What does the title have to do with Diego's intention to label everything?

Diego's intention is to organize his life by labeling everything. This "solution" will be temporary because it only lasts as long as the labels do, which won't be long.

Common Core State Standards

Questions 1–3, 5: Literature 1. Cite textual evidence to support analysis of what the text says explicitly as well as inferences drawn from the text.
Question 4: Literature 3. Describe how a particular story's or drama's plot unfolds in a series of episodes as well as how the characters respond or change as the plot moves toward a resolution.

Name _____

Read the selection. Then answer the questions that follow.

Redistricting Hits Franklin

As you know, some of Franklin Middle School's current seventh graders will not be	14
returning next fall. They will be heading instead to Kenton, the new middle school, to	29
attend eighth grade. The School Board's redistricting plan was decided last year, and	42
only two changes have been made. Students living in Sylvan Heights will go to Kenton,	57
and those living in Pine Forest will stay at Franklin. (In the original plan, the opposite	73
was true.)	75
The construction of Kenton was due to be completed this July. The winter has been	90
mild, allowing work to remain on schedule. An opening ceremony will be held in the	105
beginning of August. I urge all of you Franklin seventh graders who will be attending	120
Kenton to accompany your parents to the ceremony.	128
Kenton's computer lab has all new equipment, and the playing fields are much	141
bigger than what we have at Franklin. Although many of you and your parents have	156
expressed concern over the change, I think you will find that your new school has much	172
to offer.	174
Principal Eve Sanders	177
Franklin Middle School	180

Turn the page.

Answer the questions below.

1 What effect might a hard winter have had on Kenton?

   A The playing fields would be much too soggy to use.

   B Kids living in Sylvan Heights would stay at Franklin.

   (C) Construction would be incomplete by the end of July.

   D The opening ceremony would have to be held at Franklin.

2 For whom, *most likely*, did Principal Eve Sanders write this selection?

   F members of the Board's redistricting committee

   (G) Franklin students who will now be going to Kenton

   H parents of students who are living in Pine Forest

   J parents of those students who be attending Franklin

3 Why does the last paragraph of Principal Sanders's letter *most likely* include information about Kenton's playing fields and computer lab?

   A to explain to readers why the School Board decided to build Kenton

   B to warn readers how very different things at Kenton are going to be

   C to show readers how much she wishes she were principal at Kenton

   (D) to tell readers going to Kenton some advantages of their new school

4 Why do you think the principal of Franklin wrote about another middle school?

Answers may vary. Possible response: The principal wanted to inform students and their parents about the upcoming opening ceremony over at Kenton, and she needed to repeat which students were going to attend another school instead of hers.

Common Core State Standards

Question 1: Informational Text 1. Cite textual evidence to support analysis of what the text says explicitly as well as inferences drawn from the text.
Questions 2–4: Informational Text 8. Trace and evaluate the argument and specific claims in a text, distinguishing claims that are supported by reasons and evidence from claims that are not.

Read the selection. Then answer the questions that follow.

Letter to the Editor

To the Readers of the *Clanton County Gazette:*	8
I am writing this letter to inform you about a recent vote by our elected county	24
officials. The Clanton County Commissioners recently voted for billboards in our	35
county to be moved farther from the highway. The billboards can be moved by the	50
owner of the property on which they stand, allowing the property owner to keep the	65
billboard permit. If the property owner chooses not to relocate the billboards, then	78
the billboard company can move them. They will then take over the permit for those	93
billboards.	94
As a fellow citizen, I think the voters ought to know about this recent revision	109
to our billboard ordinance. This revision undoes a law established by the 1997	122
Commissioners, who decided that, ultimately, Clanton County would be better off	133
with *no* billboards blocking the beautiful scenery that draws travelers here in the first	147
place. That law, supported by the community, was intended to promote the gradual	160
disappearance of billboards. No *new* billboards were to be built and no *new* permits	174
granted. Standing billboards could remain standing until they wore out. That law	186
forbade upgrading these signs. They could be maintained, but not improved.	197
The Commissioners' most recent decision is likely to mean that the billboard	209
companies will rebuild and improve their billboards when they move them farther from	222
the highway. In other words, unsightly billboards seem less and less likely to disappear.	236
I want to convince the Commissioners to reconsider their recent vote. I hope that you	251
will join me by asking our Commissioners to reconsider their decision so that we can	266
return our community's highways to their natural beauty, without interference from	277
billboards.	278
Respectfully,	279
Tomás Salazar	281

Turn the page.

Answer the questions below.

1 What does the author think could happen to the county's tourist industry if the recently passed ordinance is left unchanged?

(A) Tourism might decrease because billboards block the scenery.

B More and more billboards might be built along the highway.

C Tourism might increase and cause more traffic and congestion.

D Billboards might be unsafe because they cannot be improved.

2 The purpose of the *second* paragraph of the letter is

F to show that voters had wanted the billboards.

(G) to provide details about the 1997 ordinance.

H to describe the Clanton County community.

J to explain how billboards are maintained.

3 Why did the author *most likely* write this letter?

(A) to inform the voters that this new ordinance has been passed

B to expose the businesses that have cheated billboard owners

C to air a disagreement with the other County Commissioners

D to alert people to the impacts that billboards have on tourism

4 What is the purpose of the *third* paragraph of the letter?

F to convince readers that all billboards are dangerous and unattractive

(G) to inform readers of the decision so they will join Salazar in his cause

H to persuade the voters to elect entirely new County Commissioners

J to explain why billboards are bad for tourism and the environment

5 Tell one sentence in the selection showing biased language. Explain the author's opinion that the sentence suggests.

Possible response: "In other words, unsightly billboards seem less and less likely to disappear." The word "unsightly" suggests that the letter's readers should find billboards ugly and undesirable, as the author does.

6 Copyright © Pearson Education, Inc., or its affiliates. All Rights Reserved.

Common Core State Standards

Questions 1–5: Informational Text 6. Determine an author's point of view or purpose in a text and explain how it is conveyed in the text. **Informational Text 8.** Trace and evaluate the argument and specific claims in a text, distinguishing claims that are supported by reasons and evidence from claims that are not.

Read the selection. Then answer the questions that follow.

Yesterday Comes Alive

Book Review | 2

    If you don't recognize the name Harriette Gillem Robinet, you're in for a great | 16

read—a bunch of them! Robinet's novels present memorable young characters who live | 29

in history-making times and who experience mysteries and adventures of their own. | 41

What you're always assured of from this productive author is an accurate account of a | 56

historical setting and a really involving plot, with characters who capture your heart | 69

and interest. | 71

    Robinet's novel _Twelve Travelers, Twenty Horses_ begins on the eve of Lincoln's | 83

1860 Presidential election on a courthouse square where slaves are being auctioned. At | 96

thirteen, Jacob has run away, has been recaptured, is put on sale again, and is purchased | 112

by a rich, young prospector, Clarence Higgenboom. They set out on the two-thousand- | 125

mile journey from Missouri to California, and Jacob becomes involved in rescuing the | 137

Pony Express from robbery. As in all of Robinet's novels, the reader gets a valuable | 152

perspective on a prime time in American history. | 160

    Robinet was born in Washington, D.C., and spent much of her childhood in Virginia. | 174

Her grandfather had been a slave there, in the household of Robert E. Lee. Robinet has | 190

graduate degrees in microbiology and now lives in Chicago. With her dozen novels, she | 204

has won a whole host of impressive awards. | 212

    Here are a few of her novels not to be missed—listed by their historic settings: | 228

The War of 1812: In _Washington City Is Burning,_ Virginia is a slave to President | 243

James Madison and his wife, Dolley. | 249

    Reconstruction times after the Civil War: In _Forty Acres and Maybe a Mule,_ | 262

Nellie and her brother are slaves who run away with a friend from the Union Army to a | 280

new farm. | 282

    The Great Fire of Chicago: In _Children of the Fire,_ Halleluia lives through the fire | 297

in 1871 and helps rebuild the city. | 304

    The Civil Rights Days of Rosa Parks: In _Walking the Bus Rider Blues,_ Alfa | 318

and Zinnia solve a mystery while supporting the nonviolent bus boycott in | 330

Montgomery, Alabama. | 332

Reviewed by Edward Passinger | 336

Turn the page.

Answer the questions below.

1 In the first paragraph, the author speaks directly to you as the reader. This creates a tone that seems

   A accusing.

   (**B**) inviting.

   C formal.

   D distant.

2 Why does the author *most likely* provide information about Robinet's life?

   F to contrast her life with those of her characters

   G to show that an author does a lot of research

   (**H**) to give an idea of the person behind the books

   J to show the experiences that made her into a writer

3 According to the selection, for what reason has Robinet received so many awards?

   A She has owned dozens of biology books.

   B She is a famous scientist and college professor.

   (**C**) She has written excellent historical novels.

   D She is living in Chicago after leaving Virginia.

4 The author lists Robinet's novels by historic setting. Why do you think he does this?

Possible response: He makes the point that Robinet's novels are not just entertaining—they also teach about history.

5 After bringing up Robinet's graduate degrees, the author stops saying more about them. Tell why you think he *most likely* does this.

Answer may vary. Possible response: Having the degrees shows you that Robinet was well educated, but since she studied microbiology, those degrees have nothing to do with what she writes about.

/ **Common Core State Standards** \

Questions 1–5: Informational Text 6. Determine an author's point of view or purpose in a text and explain how it is conveyed in the text.
Informational Text 8. Trace and evaluate the argument and specific claims in a text, distinguishing claims that are supported by reasons and evidence from claims that are not.

Read the selection. Then answer the questions that follow.

A Good Trade

As he walked home from school, Jeff's stomach growled. Lunch had been around	13
noon, and it was already four o'clock. Jeff passed several convenience stores, but had	28
no money with him.	31
Then he saw the manager of the new health food store removing heavy cardboard	45
boxes from a van parked in the alley.	53
"Do you need some help?" Jeff asked.	60
"I sure do," the woman said, wiping her forehead. "Thanks for the offer."	73
Jeff jumped into the van and in fifteen minutes, with both of them working, two	88
dozen boxes of peanut butter were stacked in the store beside the bins of brown rice.	104
Jeff was about to leave when the manager reached into a cooler and handed him a	120
sandwich and a cold bottle of juice. "I hope you like tuna, avocado, and sprouts on	136
whole wheat?" she said, reaching for a bottle of juice for herself.	148
"How did you know? It's my favorite," Jeff grinned.	157

Turn the page.

Answer the questions below.

1 Jeff's main problem as this story begins is that he is

  A sleepy.

  B angry.

  (C) hungry.

  D bored.

2 What happens when Jeff sees the woman unloading the truck?

  F He has to walk around the truck.

  G He asks for a job.

  H He drinks a bottle of juice.

  (J) He offers to help her.

3 Why does the woman give Jeff a sandwich?

  A because she feels sorry for him

  B because he asked for it

  C to try the new bread

  (D) as a reward for his work

4 What lesson can readers learn from Jeff's actions?

Possible response: Helping others when you see them in need can bring unexpected rewards.

Common Core State Standards

Questions 1–3: **Literature 3.** Describe how a particular story's or drama's plot unfolds in a series of episodes as well as how the characters respond or change as the plot moves toward a resolution. **Question 4: Literature 2.** Determine a theme or central idea of a text and how it is conveyed through particular details; provide a summary of the text distinct from personal opinions or judgments.

Name _____

Read the selection. Then answer the questions that follow.

The Gap

Evan, Martin, and Josh have their own band. Evan plays lead guitar, Martin plays	14
bass, and Josh sings. They take their music so seriously that they get together three or	30
four times a week and practice. They dream of performing at the local Youth Center,	45
but there's a gap. They need a drummer.	53
"My cousin plays drums," Martin offers after a very long practice.	64
"He also lives a hundred miles away," Josh groans. "Be real."	75
"Would you guys consider my sister Kate?" Evan suggests, packing up his guitar and	89
amplifier. "She's always begging to practice with us."	97
"I've seen your sister dance," Martin says. "She's got no rhythm at all!"	110
Evan admits this is true. Just because his sister learns most things quickly doesn't	124
mean she could learn to play drums.	131
The three musicians decide to post a notice on the bulletin board at the music store	147
downtown. It just announces, "Drummer Wanted," and includes Evan's phone number.	158
On Wednesday, when they post it, the three friends wonder if anyone will call. By	173
Sunday, Evan has received nine phone calls about the notice.	183
"I guess there are more drummers than we realized," Martin observes, studying the	196
list of names and phone numbers.	202
"Let's start calling," Josh says, grabbing the phone.	210
The boys call all nine drummers. Based on these conversations, they decide to ask	224
seven of them to audition. During the next two weeks, they spend practice time with all	240
seven, who have different skills and styles. Next, they ask three of them to come back	256
for another practice. The whole process takes nearly a month.	266
It's a hard choice, but their new band, called *The Gap,* has four members—including	281
a new drummer named Colleen—and a $400 gig at the Youth Center next weekend.	296

Turn the page.

Answer the questions below.

1 Which sentence is the best summary of this story's plot?

(A) A band finds a drummer.

B Three musicians form a band.

C A band holds auditions.

D The Youth Center has a show.

2 What is the conflict faced by Evan, Martin, and Josh?

F They don't play very well.

G They can't find work.

H They can't hire Martin's cousin.

(J) They need another band member.

3 What happens after the boys hang up a notice?

A No one calls.

(B) Many people call.

C Evan's sister answers the ad.

D Only one person calls.

4 Which event is part of the rising action of the story?

F Josh becomes the lead singer.

(G) The boys hold auditions for drummers.

H Three boys decide to form a band.

J The Gap performs at the Youth Center.

5 What is an important theme the author wants us to learn from this story?

Answers may vary. Possible response: Completing each step toward a goal may take a long time, but reaching that goal makes the effort worth it.

> **Common Core State Standards**

Questions 1–4: Literature 3. Describe how a particular story's or drama's plot unfolds in a series of episodes as well as how the characters respond or change as the plot moves toward a resolution. **Question 5: Literature 2.** Determine a theme or central idea of a text and how it is conveyed through particular details; provide a summary of the text distinct from personal opinions or judgments.

Name _____

Read the selection. Then answer the questions that follow.

What a Waste

The Raymond Middle School Ecology Club meets every month. In September, they	12
choose a goal they work toward all year. This year, they chose "Improve the practice of	28
'Reduce, Recycle, and Reuse' in our school cafeteria."	36
First, the club conducted a waste inventory. After a typical day, volunteers in rubber	50
gloves sorted the waste in the cafeteria garbage cans. It was a messy job,	64
but everyone laughed as they worked. The results were as follows: 13.5 pounds of	78
wasted food, 7.5 pounds of paper, 117 plastic utensils, 29 returnable glass bottles, and	92
43 returnable cans.	95
Based on this study, club members estimated that in the 180 days of the school year,	111
the cafeteria generated more than a ton of wasted food. In addition, students were	125
throwing away more than $600 worth of returnable bottles and cans, about 21,000	138
plastic forks and spoons, and 1,350 pounds of recyclable paper.	148
To address this waste, the club built permanent recycling bins. Each one was	161
colorfully painted and clearly labeled so that no one would be confused about where	175
to throw trash. Daily, club members bagged returnable bottles and cans. Weekly, the	188
advisor and two volunteers returned them to a local redemption center. Other volunteers	201
bagged paper and delivered it to the town's recycling center. Still others made	214
connections with local farmers to collect waste food at the end of every school day for	230
both compost and animal feed.	235
In addition, the Ecology Club made a huge sign that explained the new system to	250
students and requested their participation. At the end of the year, Club members agreed	264
it was their best project ever. In addition to improving their school's awareness and	278
recycling more than two tons of waste, they raised more than $500 for next year's	293
project.	294

Turn the page.

Answer the questions below.

1 **Which sentence is the best summary of this story's plot?**

   A The Raymond Middle School Ecology Club meets monthly.

   B The cafeteria generates more than a ton of waste food in a year.

   (C) An ecology club begins a recycling program in the school cafeteria.

   D Ecology clubs are set up in several communities.

2 **Based on the selection, one result of the club's project was that**

   F other schools started their own groups.

   G many students became new members.

   H teachers helped sort through the bins.

   (J) it will have a different project next year.

3 **Which statement is a theme of this story?**

   A Problems are solved only when solutions are based on teamwork.

   (B) People working together toward a goal can solve big problems.

   C People wanting to change their systems need to put up huge signs.

   D Efforts to change other people's behavior are mostly useless.

4 **How is the waste inventory important to the plot of this story?**

The waste inventory is important because it shows that there was a need for more recycling. It proves that a lot of food, paper, plastic, and returnables were being wasted in the school's cafeteria on a typical day.

5 **How does the author present the problem in this story?**

The problem presented in this story is the waste being generated in the school cafeteria. The author presents this problem in the title, "What a Waste," and then in the second paragraph which contains specific details, in the form of statistics about this waste.

Common Core State Standards

Questions 1–4: **Literature 3.** Describe how a particular story's or drama's plot unfolds in a series of episodes as well as how the characters respond or change as the plot moves toward a resolution. **Question 5: Literature 2.** Determine a theme or central idea of a text and how it is conveyed through particular details; provide a summary of the text distinct from personal opinions or judgments.

Name _____

Read the selection. Then answer the questions that follow.

Yours Alone

Look at the tips of your fingers. Can you see the little ridges? These ridges, called	16
fingerprints, are yours alone. No two people have the same prints, and each print leads	31
to only one person. Also, fingerprints do not change throughout your lifetime. For this	45
reason, they are the most interesting part of your hands.	55
There are three types of fingerprints. Arch prints have straight lines from one side of	70
the finger to the other. Loop prints have lines that curve in a horseshoe turn. In whorl	87
prints, the lines make circles. Today, the FBI has more than two hundred million prints	102
on file. It is the largest collection in the world.	112
Police use fingerprints to catch criminals. A person leaves fingerprints on things he	125
or she touches. Police gather these prints by dusting things with chemicals that make	139
the prints visible. They take pictures of the prints and enlarge them. They send the	154
pictures to the FBI. Computers show whether they match any prints in the FBI files. If	170
they do, police can name that person without a doubt.	180
As you can see, fingerprints are a police officer's best tool.	191

Turn the page.

Answer the questions below.

1 Which of these is a statement of opinion about fingerprints?

   A Police use fingerprints to catch criminals.

   (B) Fingerprints are a police officer's best tool.

   C The FBI has more than two hundred million prints on file.

   D Arch prints have straight lines.

2 What does a police officer do first at a crime scene?

   (F) dusts objects for fingerprints

   G takes pictures of the fingerprints

   H sends the pictures to the FBI

   J waits to see whether the prints match any on file

3 Which of these sentences expresses the writer's opinion?

   A Fingerprints are yours alone.

   B No two people have the same fingerprint.

   C Fingerprints do not change throughout your lifetime.

   (D) Fingerprints are the most interesting part of your hands.

4 Is the following sentence a statement of fact or opinion? Give the reason for your answer.

The first person to use fingerprints to identify people was William J. Hershel, a government official in India, in 1858.

It is a statement of fact. It contains a specific name and date. I can look up this fact in an encyclopedia and discover whether it is true or false.

Common Core State Standards

Questions 1, 2, 4: Informational Text 8. Trace and evaluate the argument and specific claims in a text, distinguishing claims that are supported by reasons and evidence from claims that are not. **Question 3: Informational Text 6.** Determine an author's point of view or purpose in a text and explain how it is conveyed in the text.

Name _____

Read the selection. Then answer the questions that follow.

My Grandmother's Pearls

At special times, my grandmother wears a beautiful necklace made of about two	13
dozen perfect white pearls. The last time I saw it, at my cousin's wedding, I decided	29
to find out more about pearls and how they are made. What I discovered is a	45
fascinating story.	47

I was surprised to learn that pearls form inside the shells of oysters, the creatures	62
that live on the ocean bottom. Unlike other gems that are dug from inside the Earth,	78
these little beauties actually grow inside living ocean creatures! Oysters make a	90
substance called *nacre* that lines the insides of their shells. When a foreign substance,	104
such as a grain of sand, enters the body of an oyster, layers of nacre form on it. As time	124
goes on, more and more layers grow. It takes years for that tiny grain to grow into a	142
perfect pearl.	144

To make a necklace like my grandmother's, you need many pearls of the same size	159
and shape. Before the last century, divers found oysters and broke them open, hoping	173
to discover pearls, a difficult task that needed both skill and luck. Most of the world's	189
natural pearl beds are in the Persian Gulf.	197

Since 1900, thanks to a Japanese inventor named Kokichi Mikimoto, people actually	209
cultivate pearls. When young oysters are three years old, trained workers pry open their	223
shells and insert tiny pellets made from mussel shells taken from the Mississippi River.	237
The oysters are then lowered into the water in cages. Four years later, the oysters are	253
opened. About one in every twenty oysters contains a perfect cultured pearl.	265

About 70 percent of the world's cultured pearls are sold in the United States, just	280
like the ones in my grandmother's beautiful necklace.	288

Turn the page.

Answer the questions below.

1 **Which of these is a statement of opinion about pearls?**

A About 70 percent of the world's cultured pearls are sold in the United States.

B Kokichi Mikimoto invented cultured pearls.

(C) Pearls are the most difficult gems to obtain.

D It requires many layers of *nacre* to make a pearl.

2 **What is the first step in making a cultured pearl?**

F Insert a tiny pellet from a mussel shell.

G Lower the oyster back into the water.

H Open the oyster and look for a pearl.

(J) Collect an oyster that is three years old.

3 **Which of these sentences appears to express the speaker's opinion?**

A My grandmother owns a pearl necklace.

(B) The story of how pearls are made is fascinating.

C Most of the world's natural pearls come from the Persian Gulf.

D Pearls grow in the shells of ocean creatures.

4 **What is the best way to verify the fact that pearls can be black, white, pink, or orange.**

F Ask the person who wrote this selection.

(G) Research pearls in a library or online.

H Go to a jewelry store and look at pearls.

J Look inside an oyster.

5 **Is the following sentence a statement of fact or opinion? Give the reason for your answer.**
Kokichi Mikimoto has been the most successful inventor in the history of Japan.

This sentence is a statement of opinion. Whether Mikimoto was successful or not might be considered factual, but whether he is "most" successful cannot be proved because it depends on how success is measured.

Common Core State Standards

Questions 1, 2, 4, 5: Informational Text 8. Trace and evaluate the argument and specific claims in a text, distinguishing claims that are supported by reasons and evidence from claims that are not. **Question 3: Informational Text 6.** Determine an author's point of view or purpose in a text and explain how it is conveyed in the text.

Name _____

Read the selection. Then answer the questions that follow.

The History of Paper
by Sarah Roosevelt

Paper is the most important invention in human history. Without it, there would be	14
no books, letters, documents, or records. Without it, there would be no governments,	27
history, or financial systems.	31
More than five thousand years ago, the Egyptians made a writing material from a	45
plant called *papyrus,* from which the word *paper* derives. They cut these reeds into thin	60
slices and then pressed them together into long scrolls. About 2000 B.C., the Egyptians	74
replaced the scrolls with sheets that they bound together, much like our modern books.	88
What we think of as paper was invented by the Chinese in A.D. 105 by a government	105
minister of public works named Ts'ai Lun. He discovered that the inner bark of the	120
mulberry tree could be broken into fibers and pounded into a flat sheet. Based on this	136
method, the Chinese also made paper out of rags, hemp, and even old fishnets.	150
The art of making paper spread from China to the Middle East. As papermakers from	165
the Middle East came to Northern Africa and then people from North Africa entered	179
Spain, papermaking spread north. For several hundred years, paper was made by hand	192
from rag pulp, but in 1798 this changed. Frenchman Nicholas Louis Robert invented a	206
machine that made paper from wood pulp in long continuous rolls rather than in small	221
batches. His invention set the stage for newspapers.	229
In 1840 a German named Friedrich Keller invented a process for grinding logs into	243
pulp, and, later, chemists added sulfurous acid to the wood as a preservative. Today,	257
most of the world's paper is made in the United States from pulp from spruce, fir,	273
hemlock, and pine trees found in the northern United States and Canada.	285
Even in this computer age, it is difficult to imagine a world—or even a day—without	302
paper.	303

Turn the page.

Answer the questions below.

1 **How does the writer begin this selection?**
- **A** She begins with specific facts about paper's popularity.
- **(B)** She offers an opinion about the importance of paper.
- **C** She describes how paper is made.
- **D** She tells a story of how paper was invented.

2 **Who invented paper as we know it?**
- **F** Friedrich Keller in Germany
- **G** Nicholas Robert in France
- **(H)** Ts'ai Lun in China
- **J** chemists in the United States

3 **Which of these sentences appears to express the writer's opinion?**
- **A** The word *paper* comes from the word *papyrus*.
- **B** Today, most of the world's paper is made in the United States.
- **C** Papermaking spread from China to the Middle East.
- **(D)** It's difficult to imagine a world without paper.

4 **Is the following sentence a statement of fact or a statement of opinion? Give the reason for your answer.**

In A.D. 105, Ts'ai Lun made paper from the inner bark of the mulberry tree.

This sentence is a statement of fact. It includes a date, a specific name, and an event from history that can be proved true.

5 **Can you tell what the writer's opinion is about recycling paper? Explain your answer.**

No. The writer says that paper in the United States is made of different trees but does not use any clue words suggesting whether that is good or bad. The writer does not mention recycling at all.

Common Core State Standards

Questions 1, 2, 4: Informational Text 8. Trace and evaluate the argument and specific claims in a text, distinguishing claims that are supported by reasons and evidence from claims that are not. **Questions 3, 5: Informational Text 6.** Determine an author's point of view or purpose in a text and explain how it is conveyed in the text.

Name _____

Read the selection. Then answer the questions that follow.

Darkness Wins

The math team met at 7:00 P.M. one evening to prepare for an upcoming tournament.	15
Michael and Susan arrived early. They spread their notebooks, practice tests, and	27
calculators all over the table. Steven and Erica showed up soon and spread out their	42
notes from the last three meets. When Ms. Donnelly, their advisor, arrived at 7:00 P.M.,	57
they had already started planning how they might best spend the next two hours.	71
At 7:05, all the lights went out and everyone groaned. "Let's wait a few minutes,"	86
Ms. Donnelly suggested, "and maybe the electricity will come back on."	97
They waited ten minutes, then fifteen. At 7:30, they agreed that it was foolish to sit	113
in the dark. They groped around the table, searching for books, backpacks, pencils,	126
calculators, and papers. They kept bumping into each other, laughing and saying	138
"Excuse me." At 7:45, when Ms. Donnelly closed the heavy classroom door, the loud	152
click echoed in the empty hallway.	158
Just as they stepped outside, the lights came on. Everyone laughed. "Should we go	172
back in?" the students asked.	177
"No," Ms. Donnelly sighed. "I've had a long day. Tonight, the darkness won."	190

Turn the page.

Answer the questions below.

1 Why did the students pack up all their materials and leave the school?

A They were to have a math tournament soon.

B The electricity came back on.

Ⓒ The electricity failed and it was too dark to see.

D Their adviser told them they didn't need to practice.

2 The climax of this story happens when

F Ms. Donnelly arrives in the classroom.

G the lights go out in the school building.

Ⓗ the lights come back on at the school.

J the door clicks loudly in the quiet hall.

3 Why did Ms. Donnelly decide not to return to the classroom?

A Everyone was groaning and complaining.

B Donna had notes from three other meets.

C No one could see to practice.

Ⓓ She was tired and ready to go home.

4 Will the electricity going out probably have a positive or negative effect on the math team's performance in the tournament? Explain your answer.

The electricity going out will probably have a negative effect on the math team's performance in the tournament because they did not have the two hours of preparation they had planned.

Common Core State Standards

Questions 1, 3, 4: Literature 1. Cite textual evidence to support analysis of what the text says explicitly as well as inferences drawn from the text.
Question 2: Literature 3. Describe how a particular story's or drama's plot unfolds in a series of episodes as well as how the characters respond or change as the plot moves toward a resolution.

Name _____

Read the selection. Then answer the questions that follow.

The Perfect Gift

Next Friday was Elisa Kendall's thirteen birthday, and her mother had offered to buy	14
her a gift. Elisa pondered, but she couldn't imagine anything she wanted or needed and	29
didn't have. Her closet was full of clothes, and she downloaded her music. She had just	45
bought hiking boots, and she didn't need soccer equipment. What she really wanted	58
was to have her closest friends over to her house to dance.	70
"Since my birthday is on a weekend, I want to throw a party," she admitted to her	87
mother, suddenly certain of her decision.	93
"That's a good idea," her mother agreed, "and I can afford about $100."	106
Elisa and her mother decided to order four jumbo pepperoni pizzas for $40, a birthday	121
cake for $10, and Elisa's favorite chips, which cost $10 for two enormous bags. "What	136
about drinks?" her mother wondered as they added up their expenses so far.	149
Elisa thought for a moment, remembering that last week she'd noticed a sign for a	164
local disk jockey that said that he'd perform at private parties for $20 an hour, and she	181
had jotted down the phone number. "We can drink water if it means we could have a	198
disk jockey for two hours," Elisa suggested, "and I've got a phone number right here."	213
"Sounds like you're a thirteen-year-old who knows what she wants," said her mother,	226
searching for the cordless phone.	231
Elisa's birthday party was the best gift she ever received. The pizza was steamy	245
and delicious, the carrot cake was moist and sweet, and the chips vanished in half an	261
hour. Best of all, the disk jockey played Elisa's favorite tunes for two solid hours, and	277
everyone danced until they were exhausted.	283
"How was it?" her mother inquired the next day as they mopped the kitchen.	297
"Fun," Elisa smiled, "just like being thirteen."	304

Turn the page.

Answer the questions below.

1 **Why do Elisa and her mother plan how much everything will cost?**

  A Elisa will be thirteen next Tuesday.

  B They plan to invite eight friends.

  C They have a budget of $100.

  D A successful party requires planning.

2 **Which of these events is an example of a flashback?**

  F Elisa asks her mother for a birthday party.

  G Elisa writes down the phone number of a disk jockey.

  H All eight friends attend the party.

  I Elisa and her mother add up the costs.

3 **Elisa and her friends were exhausted because**

  A they had been in school all day and then at the party.

  B they weren't used to parties.

  C they danced to all the good music the disk jockey played for them.

  D they ate too much.

4 **"Elisa has plenty of clothes" is a cause. What is the effect in the story?**

  F Elisa wants more clothes anyway.

  G Elisa doesn't want clothes as a gift.

  H Elisa wants to give some of her clothes away.

  I Elisa received clothes for her twelfth birthday.

5 **What is a theme that the author wants us to learn?**

**Answers may vary. Possible response: Sometimes with careful**

**planning, you can get the perfect gift.**

Common Core State Standards

Questions 1–4: Literature 1. Cite textual evidence to support analysis of what the text says explicitly as well as inferences drawn from the text.
Question 5: Literature 2. Determine a theme or central idea of a text and how it is conveyed through particular details; provide a summary of the text distinct from personal opinions or judgments.

Name _____

Read the selection. Then answer the questions that follow.

A Chilly Lesson

Nick shivered. His fingers felt like ice cubes, and his teeth were starting to chatter. "I	16
guess Mom was right," he thought. His mom had warned him that a dangerous blizzard	31
was approaching, but Nick just thought she was being overprotective, as usual.	43
The day had started out sunny and brisk, with just a few ominous clouds looming	58
on the horizon. Nick had just joined the Eagle Conservation Society, and he was	72
determined to locate at least one eagle's nest today. His task was to help document the	88
number of nests in Landcrest State Park. So far he had identified two nests, and today	104
he was hoping to find another one.	111
Nick squinted toward the canyon rim. "That looks like a prime spot for a nest,"	126
he thought. "I know the conservation society president said we should stay on the	140
trails, but I really want to find another nest. I want to find more nests than any other	158
volunteer!" So Nick set out, leaving the trail behind.	167
As he hiked, snowflakes started to swirl around him. Soon the snow was so heavy	182
that Nick could hardly see anything at all. He turned back toward the trail, but he saw	199
nothing familiar. He knew he was in trouble. He didn't have a jacket, or food, or water.	216
Nick huddled behind a boulder and thought about his mistakes. "Maybe I shouldn't	229
have been so worried about being the best conservation society volunteer," he thought.	242
Suddenly Nick heard a voice in the distance, calling his name. He turned toward the	257
sound and shouted. Within minutes, his mom and a park ranger appeared. "Maybe next	271
time you'll listen to your mom," said the park ranger with a wry smile.	285

Turn the page.

Answer the questions below.

1 For what reason had Nick ignored his mom's warning about the weather?

   A He wanted to be the one who found the most nests.

   B He was in a hurry to go on his hike through the park.

   C He decided that the weather looked sunny and safe.

   (D) He thought she was being an overprotective mother.

2 What happened to make Nick decide to leave the trail?

   (F) He saw a likely spot for an eagle's nest.

   G He wanted to find baby eagles before it snowed.

   H He thought he would know his way back.

   J He felt the president could not find anything out.

3 What worried Nick about his mistakes?

   A He thought his mom would want to buy him some new gloves and a jacket.

   (B) He knew he was in a dangerous situation because he had been so foolish.

   C He thought another volunteer was going to find more nests than he had.

   D He was afraid the society's president would be angry that he left the trail.

4 Tell one way the author uses foreshadowing to give readers clues about what will happen in the story.

Possible response: The author describes the clouds as "ominous" to help you know something bad is going to happen. You can predict that Nick will be facing dangerous weather because of those clouds.

5 What do you think is the *most likely* thing that Nick will learn as the result of this experience?

Possible response: Nick will learn that being the "best" volunteer is not as important as listening to good advice from others, and in the future he won't let his pride get the best of him.

Common Core State Standards

Questions 1–3: Literature 1. Cite textual evidence to support analysis of what the text says explicitly as well as inferences drawn from the text.
Questions 4, 5: Literature 3. Describe how a particular story's or drama's plot unfolds in a series of episodes as well as how the characters respond or change as the plot moves toward a resolution.

Read the selection. Then answer the questions that follow.

Two Kinds of Terns

Terns are huge sea birds, well-known for their powers of flight. Their wingspan can	14
reach more than four feet. As terns fly, they dive into the sea to catch fish. Two kinds of	33
terns live on Earth: Arctic terns live at the North Pole and Antarctic terns live near the	50
South Pole.	52
Antarctic terns dig holes in the bare Earth in October. Their eggs are brown and tan	68
like the sand around them. The parents fly to and from the nest, returning with fish	84
for their young. Antarctic terns breed in Antarctica during the summer (November to	97
January) and then fly to warmer seas near South America during the winter (June to	112
August).	113
Their northern cousin, the Arctic tern, breeds near the North Pole in the summer	127
(June to August) and then flies all the way south to the Antarctic to enjoy *another*	143
summer from November to January! They fly over fifteen thousand miles, farther than	156
any other bird. On their southern vacation, Arctic terns feed at sea before returning	170
north in March.	173
They may look alike, but the two kinds of terns mate in different parts of the year, at	191
different poles, and only with others like themselves.	199

Turn the page.

Answer the questions below.

1 **What is the main idea of this selection?**
- (A) The two kinds of terns are similar but different.
- **B** Terns are huge sea birds.
- **C** Terns are in danger of becoming extinct.
- **D** Arctic terns and Antarctic terns are the same birds.

2 **Which of the following true statements supports the main idea?**
- **F** Scientists who study birds are called ornithologists.
- **G** Very few animals live in Antarctica.
- (H) Both types of terns are brown and have broad wings.
- **J** At the South Pole, winter lasts from November to January.

3 **The selection indicates that terns**
- **A** are very shy birds.
- (B) have amazing powers of flight.
- **C** only live at the South Pole.
- **D** only eat plants.

4 **What would be a probable effect if an Arctic tern did not fly south in September or October?**

**Possible response: It might not survive the cold of Arctic
winter. It might not find enough food to eat during the winter.**

Common Core State Standards

Questions 1–3: Informational Text 2. Determine a central idea of a text and how it is conveyed through particular details; provide a summary of the text distinct from personal opinions or judgments. Question 4: Informational Text 1. Cite textual evidence to support analysis of what the text says explicitly as well as inferences drawn from the text.

Gold

Read the selection. Then answer the questions that follow.

A New Kind of Writing

Louis Braille was born in 1809, in the village of Coupvray near Paris, France. His	15
father made shoes and harnesses. As a child, Louis was playing with an awl in his	31
father's workshop when it slipped and damaged one eye, permanently blinding it.	43
By the time he was four, the sight in Braille's other eye was damaged by infection,	59
and the boy lost his sight completely. However, he showed great promise in school,	73
especially in music, and was enrolled in the Royal Institution for the Blind in Paris. He	89
learned to read by feeling raised print on paper, the most popular system at the time.	105
This reading went very slowly, however, because it was difficult to tell the letters apart	120
by touch. This method also didn't offer a way for blind people to write.	134
In 1821, Louis Braille learned about a new kind of writing developed for the French	149
military called "night writing." It used a system of twelve raised dots in various	163
patterns to represent certain sounds. Braille saw a great possibility for the use of	177
this system for the blind, and spent the next few years experimenting with it and	192
simplifying it. The system he invented used just six dots, first for words and letters	207
and later for math and music.	213
The first book in Braille was published in 1829, but the system didn't catch on for	229
a very long time. When Louis Braille died in 1852, the magnitude of his achievement	244
hadn't yet been recognized, and the system he invented wasn't widely known. Today,	257
Braille is used all over the world in almost every language on the planet, and the man	274
who invented it is honored as a great hero of France and one of the world's great	291
inventors.	292

Turn the page.

Answer the questions below.

1 The main idea of the second paragraph is
(A) Braille learned to read letters by touch.
B Braille lost his sight in an accident.
C Braille invented a new kind of writing.
D Braille went to school in Paris.

2 Which of the following details does not support the idea that the system used at the Royal Academy could be improved?
F The letters could not be used to write.
G Many letters felt alike.
H Reading went very slowly.
(J) The alphabet was already familiar.

3 The last paragraph supports the idea that
A Braille is one of the only inventors to become a hero.
B it took more than twenty-five years for the Braille system to catch on.
(C) Braille's achievement had a far-reaching global impact.
D nearly everyone in the world can read Braille.

4 Which of the following expresses a broad main idea of this selection?
F Using Braille is good for everyone, blind or not.
(G) Physical impairments can lead to great inventions.
H Many people lose their eyesight because of infection.
J The French military, not Louis Braille, invented this new kind of language.

5 Why was the military system of raised letters probably called "night writing"?

This system was probably called "night writing" because soldiers could read it even in the dark. To read it, they used their sense of touch rather than their sense of sight.

Common Core State Standards

Questions 1–4: Informational Text 2. Determine a central idea of a text and how it is conveyed through particular details; provide a summary of the text distinct from personal opinions or judgments. **Question 5: Informational Text 1.** Cite textual evidence to support analysis of what the text says explicitly as well as inferences drawn from the text.

Read the selection. Then answer the questions that follow.

A Gem of a Park

Crystal Lake Park in Harrison is a gem. The first thing you see is two sets of green | 18

painted bleachers overlooking a softball field. In the spring, you'll see boys and/or girls | 32

learning to pitch or adults enjoying a game of softball. Nearby, a basketball court holds | 47

ramps used by local skateboarders and BMX bikers. The "Food Booth" sells popcorn, | 60

hot dogs, candy, and soft drinks. Children swing, slide, and climb on new playground | 74

equipment. A dozen picnic tables, each with its own grill, hide among clumps of | 88

birches. The park's most dramatic feature is the clean, gently sloping beach, full of | 102

grandparents under umbrellas and toddlers with plastic buckets. On hot summer days, | 114

the parking lot is always full. | 120

Crystal Lake Park originated in 1972, when voters approved funds to turn the | 133

Victorian Hunt Manor into a park. The property had been purchased by the town in | 148

1968. Most of the construction took place during 1973. In 1982, the Harrison Men's | 162

Club held a fundraising drive to build and fence a basketball court at the park. With | 178

help from the Lions Club and lots of volunteer labor, the town erected its own hoops. In | 195

July of 1983, Ken Stackpole donated a new scoreboard. In 1985, the Old Home Days | 210

Committee voted to construct the wooden booth at the park. In 1987, the Crystal Lake | 225

boat ramp was proposed. It was completed in November of 1989. | 236

In 1999, most of the park's old metal playground equipment was declared unsafe and | 250

removed. The Playground Committee formed and began to raise money and draw plans. | 263

Through the generous support of Harrison taxpayers, businesses, and organizations, | 273

$41,000 was raised. In May and September of 2000, community volunteers built a new | 287

modern playground that will be safe for many years to come. | 298

Turn the page.

Answer the questions below.

1 You might expect to find this selection in a

A textbook about lakes and rivers.

(B) history of Harrison.

C brochure about the Victoria Hunt Manor.

D letter from the Playground Committee to local businesses.

2 Which of the following activities is not mentioned as being available in Crystal Lake Park?

F softball

G cookouts

H swimming

(J) tennis

3 Why did the town decide to build a new playground?

A A flood had damaged the old playground.

B The site of the old playgound was too uneven.

(C) The old playground equipment was no longer safe.

D Everyone preferred the look of more modern equipment.

4 What about the park's location makes it more special than a park in the middle of town?

Possible response: The park is next to a lake, which allows for more activities and a nice view.

5 Is the author's love for the park shared by many people? Use details from the selection to explain your answer.

Possible response: Yes, many people love the park. The selection describes people of all ages spending time there and tells how different groups have worked to improve the park.

Common Core State Standards

Questions 1–3: Informational Text 2. Determine a central idea of a text and how it is conveyed through particular details; provide a summary of the text distinct from personal opinions or judgments. **Question 4: Informational Text 1.** Cite textual evidence to support analysis of what the text says explicitly as well as inferences drawn from the text. **Question 5: Informational Text 6.** Determine an author's point of view or purpose in a text and explain how it is conveyed in the text.

Name _____

Read the selection. Then answer the questions that follow.

Is Chocolate Bugging You?

Next time you want chocolate, think about the bugs that likely helped make it.	14
Chocolate-covered candies have a special shine and can sit in their wrapping for up	28
to a year staying fresh and tasty. How did they get so glossy and lasting? *Shellac,* a	45
substance that comes from insects. Shellac gives candies shine and keeps them fresh. It	59
blocks out moisture and oxygen, which break down fat and ruin flavor.	71
Shellac comes from forests in Southeast Asia. Tiny insects suck the sap from trees	85
and secrete a sticky amber fluid called *lac,* which helps the females cling to branches.	100
The branches covered in lac are taken and crushed. The broken-down material is	113
washed and strained. The harvested shellac is used in many items we might see every	128
day, such as doll hair and floor finish. It is also used in the outer coating of pills, fruits,	147
and colored candies.	150

Turn the page.

Answer the questions below.

1 Which step most likely occurs right *after* the broken-down branch material is strained?

A The female insects fly away to other trees in the forest.

B Shellac is added to it next to make it more sticky.

Ⓒ The lac is separated from the wood and processed further.

D Oxygen, moisture, and bugs are then blocked out.

2 What happens right *before* the insects produce lac?

F Female insects are covered in lac.

G Insects suck a sticky amber fluid.

H Female insects cling to branches.

Ⓙ Insects suck the sap from the trees.

3 Which of the following states the main idea of the *first* paragraph?

A People often consume bug juice without knowing it.

B Insects protect your food from moisture and oxygen.

Ⓒ Shellac from insects keeps chocolate shiny and fresh.

D Candy can be wrapped up for a year and still be good.

4 Suppose that some chocolate-covered candy tastes stale and strange. Based on the selection, what do you think had happened to it *before* you tasted it?

Possible response: The candy's shellac coating probably got cracks in it and let in some moisture and oxygen. That would have broken down the fat and changed the flavor of the candy.

___

Common Core State Standards

Questions 1–3: Informational Text 2. Determine a central idea of a text and how it is conveyed through particular details; provide a summary of the text distinct from personal opinions or judgments. **Question 4: Informational Text 1.** Cite textual evidence to support analysis of what the text says explicitly as well as inferences drawn from the text.

Name _____

Read the selection. Then answer the questions that follow.

Lacy of the Lone Star State

Each state has its own established symbols, including a state bird, state tree, state | 14

flower, and state motto. Nine states have also established an official breed of dog. | 28

Maryland was first, choosing the Chesapeake Bay Retriever in 1964. Pennsylvania | 39

closely followed, choosing the Great Dane in 1965, and Virginia chose the American | 52

Foxhound in 1966. In the 1970s and 1980s, a handful of states, including Wisconsin, | 66

North and South Carolina, Louisiana, and Massachusetts, each chose a breed to | 78

represent them. In the last two decades, the only state to select an official state breed | 94

has been Texas. | 97

In 2005, Texas appointed the Blue Lacy, a compact and athletic dog good at | 111

managing cattle, pigs, and even chickens, to represent the Lone Star state. Texas | 124

Ranchers George, Ewin, Frank, and Harry Lacy created the breed in the 1850s, | 137

supposedly using Greyhound, scenthound, and coyote stock. All Lacys carry a rare | 149

blue-color gene, though they can be blue, red, or tricolor. The Lacy became a popular | 164

ranch dog because it was smart, fast, willing to work, and easy to handle. Over the next | 181

hundred years, Lacys were a common sight on ranches all across the Southwest. But | 195

when the use of dogs on ranches declined, the Blue Lacy nearly disappeared as a breed. | 211

Since 1975, efforts have been made to save this Texas original. Today, Lacys number | 225

more than a thousand. Most registered Lacys are born in Texas and belong to Texans, | 240

though admirers of the breed can be found in all states. | 251

Some Lacys are still used on ranches, though they've turned out to be such good | 266

search-and-rescue dogs, athletic companions, and family pets, they're as likely to be | 278

found in backyards, neighborhoods, and dog parks. They are part of Texas's ranching | 291

heritage—and part of its modern life. | 298

Turn the page.

Answer the questions below.

1 Which of the following states the main idea of the *first* paragraph?

 A Texas is one of the few states that have an official state breed.

 (B) Some states have picked a specific dog breed to represent them.

 C All U.S. states have their own flowers, birds, trees, and mottos.

 D States always choose a breed of dog that was developed there.

2 According to the selection, which state was the *first* to choose an official state dog?

 F Texas

 G Pennsylvania

 (H) Maryland

 J Virginia

3 What was happening with the Lacy breed between 1850 and 1950?

 A Efforts were made to keep Lacys from disappearing.

 B The number of Lacys used as ranching dogs decreased.

 C Ranchers combined different dogs to create a Lacy.

 (D) The use of Lacys as ranching dogs became widespread.

4 Which characteristic of the Lacy has become evident *most recently*?

 F excellent stock herder

 (G) good family companion

 H willing to work hard

 J easy to train and handle

5 Lacys were once popular ranching dogs across the Southwest. Tell two major steps in the history of the breed between then and now.

Possible response: The breed nearly died out when Texas ranchers stopped using dogs so much. Then the breed started doing new jobs, like being search-and-rescue team members, and their numbers are now increasing.

Common Core State Standards

Questions 1–4: Informational Text 2. Determine a central idea of a text and how it is conveyed through particular details; provide a summary of the text distinct from personal opinions or judgments. Question 5: Informational Text 1. Cite textual evidence to support analysis of what the text says explicitly as well as inferences drawn from the text.

Read the selection. Then answer the questions that follow.

A Short History of Tomatoes

No one knows where, exactly, the original tomato came from, though it's long been | 14

grouped in the New World (American) plant family, with the eggplant, potato, and chili | 28

pepper. These plants spread throughout the world after Christopher Columbus brought | 39

their seeds back to Spain in the late fiftheen century. As for the tomato, people aren't | 55

sure whether Columbus or another Spanish explorer, Cortés, first took its seeds to Spain. | 69

Scientists have found evidence of many crops on pottery shards up to 10,000 years | 83

old, but they have yet to determine where the first little red fruit for ketchup grew. The | 100

tomato appears to have come from a wild version in the Andes Mountains that was | 115

brought to Mexico, "tamed," and became a popular crop. Scientists have identified | 127

about thirteen species of wild tomato, and consider another four to be close relatives. | 141

None of these plants, however, was the "Mother Tomato." The tiny currant tomato is | 155

the closest relative, but many scientists think its genetics split from the genetics of the | 170

Spaniards' tomato more than 1.4 million years ago. | 178

Many sizes and shapes of tomatoes are available now. So what happened once this | 192

juicy red treasure reached Europe? For almost two hundred years (1650s to the early | 206

1800s), people in Europe and North America experimented with different types of | 218

tomato plants, trying to breed plants that would produce bigger and better tasting | 231

tomatoes. The results were what, today, we call "heirloom tomatoes." People see these | 244

tomato types, which have charming names like Aunt Gertie's Gold and Banana Legs, | 257

as symbolic of history and pioneer gardeners. Scientists, however, see them as poorly | 270

bred. Modern tomatoes like Beefsteak and Early Girl resist diseases better and yield | 283

more fruit. Modern tomatoes are *hybrids,* which means their seeds will not produce | 296

new plants. The seeds of the heirlooms can be passed down generation to generation. | 310

Seed Savers Exchange in Decorah, Iowa, established in 1975, allows members all over | 323

the world to preserve and share a variety of such heirloom plants. | 335

Turn the page.

Answer the questions below.

1 What is the main idea of this selection?

A Christopher Columbus found many new vegetables on his trip to America.

B The tomato, eggplant, potato, and chili pepper belong to the same plant family.

C Many of the vegetables we eat today have been around for thousands of years.

(D) The tomato, a fruit of unknown origin, has been popular since its discovery.

2 According to the selection, where did the tomato travel *right after* Spaniards discovered it in the New World?

F Iowa

(G) Spain

H Andes Mountains

J European countries

3 Which of the following events was the *first one* to occur?

A Hybrid tomatoes were bred.

B Heirloom tomatoes were bred.

(C) The genes of the currant tomato and the Spaniards' tomato split.

D The Seed Savers Exchange was established in Decorah, Iowa.

4 Based on the selection, tell three events that should *most likely* appear on a timeline of heirloom tomatoes.

Possible response: First, from the 1650s to the 1800s, people combined tomato plants to develop new kinds of tomatoes. Then, when there were modern hybrids, those "new" tomatoes became outdated. Finally, in 1975, Seed Savers Exchange set up a "seed bank," and after that people could get some of the old-fashioned tomato seeds again.

5 "A Short History of Tomatoes" tells how this fruit became widely known. List in order the steps the tomato has taken to come from the wild to today's world.

Possible response: A wild version, growing in the Andes, was discovered and taken to Mexico, where it was then cultivated as a crop. Later, Spaniards found it and took it to Spain. Then people in Europe liked it and made it grow even better, and they took it all over the world.

/ **Common Core State Standards** \

Questions 1–3, 5: Informational Text 2. Determine a central idea of a text and how it is conveyed through particular details; provide a summary of the text distinct from personal opinions or judgments. **Question 4: Informational Text 1.** Cite textual evidence to support analysis of what the text says explicitly as well as inferences drawn from the text.

Name _____

Read the selection. Then answer the questions that follow.

The Smallest Poems

Haiku (hi-koo) are very small poems. They were invented by Japanese poets in the	14
sixteenth century. These little poems, only three lines long, have seventeen syllables.	26
There are five syllables in the first line, seven in the second line, and five again in the	44
third line.	46
Haiku are about single moments of experience. They are often about nature or the	60
seasons. The best ones offer surprise and delight to their readers. Here are three	74
modern haiku:	76
A full moon tonight:	80
I will howl! I will hunt in	87
the woods with the owl.	92
The cat's face: wise with	97
two golden mirrors like her	102
cup and saucer eyes.	106
The last of the snow	111
slides off the metal roof: Spring	117
swallowing Winter.	119
The next time you see something in the world that gets your attention, try expressing	134
it in a haiku. They are as much fun to write as they are to read.	150

Turn the page.

Answer the questions below.

1 **Why did the author include three haiku?**

   A to make her readers laugh out loud

   B to share her feelings about her pets

   C to get the reader's attention

   (D) to show examples of what haiku can be about

2 **In the first two paragraphs, the author**

   F shares Japanese history.

   (G) defines and explains haiku.

   H compares cats and cups.

   J discusses several different kinds of poems.

3 **It is likely that the author wrote "The Smallest Poems"** *mostly*

   A to explain to readers why haiku are so complex and difficult.

   B to persuade readers to use only haiku to write about their lives.

   (C) to entertain readers with the cleverness and appeal of haiku.

   D to help readers figure out the meaning of three very old haiku.

4 **Look at the three haiku in the selection. Choose one of them, and explain how it is different from the other two.**

Answers may vary. Possible response: The first haiku has a first-person narrator ("I"), but the other two do not have any narrator like that.

Common Core State Standards

Questions 1–3: Informational Text 6. Determine an author's point of view or purpose in a text and explain how it is conveyed in the text. **Question 4: Informational Text 1.** Cite textual evidence to support analysis of what the text says explicitly as well as inferences drawn from the text.

Read the selection. Then answer the questions that follow.

How Walls Can Talk

For decades, scientists have used the data from self-reports—information people	11
provided about themselves—to learn about human personality traits. Recently, Dr.	22
Sam Gosling decided to gather data from a different source: the spaces that people are	37
living in. Gosling figured that the things we do in our homes or offices would provide	53
information about our personalities. He calls this information "behavioral residue,"	63
which, he explains, is the visible part of our actions. And our actions, Gosling says,	78
"are the meat of everyday personality."	84
In his recent book *Snoop: What Your Stuff Says About You,* Gosling describes his	98
findings. Gosling reports that some of the conclusions people tend to leap to about	112
others can be wrong. For example, if we see an office or home that is kept in very	130
good order, with books and music arranged from A–Z or according to size, we might	146
conclude that the person there is very responsible and reliable. However, Gosling found	159
that this feature of an environment instead indicates that the person strongly prefers to	173
be in control. That is, keeping one's things in good order has little to do with a person's	191
dependability or sense of responsibility.	196
When Gosling's "snooping" team visits the living space of one of their subjects, they	210
look to see whether the rooms are colorful, whether they get a lot of natural light, and	227
how they've been decorated (that is, with a theme like sports or animals). The team also	243
obtains a self-report. Each subject answers the questions on a formal personality test.	256
Reports from close friends are also provided. So far, Gosling and his team have found	271
a good match among the person people think themselves to be, the one whom their	286
friends know, and what their living spaces tell about them.	296

Turn the page.

Answer the questions below.

1 Based on the *first* paragraph, how are self-reports and the traces we leave in our living spaces alike?

   A Both are less accurate than data from personality tests.

   B They provide information we have no control over.

   (C) Both can provide information about personality traits.

   D They are the visible results of all our daily actions.

2 The writer of this article assumes readers will find Dr. Gosling's data on personality

   F unimportant and ordinary.

   (G) interesting and amusing.

   H complicated and complete.

   J inaccurate and confusing.

3 How does the writer of this article *probably* want you to judge the "snooping" team's methods?

   (A) thorough

   B careless

   C unfair

   D useless

4 The author *most likely* wrote the article, "How Walls Can Talk,"

   F to teach readers how to leave the fewest traces behind.

   G to warn readers that they ought to be keeping their rooms neat.

   H to persuade readers to research their own living places.

   (J) to show readers entertaining things their spaces tell about them.

5 When writing this article, the author *probably* expected some people to like it more than others. What readers do you think would enjoy it the most?

   Answers may vary. Possible response: The author probably thought that people who are curious about themselves and others would enjoy this article the most.

Common Core State Standards

Questions 1, 5: Informational Text 1. Cite textual evidence to support analysis of what the text says explicitly as well as inferences drawn from the text.
Questions 2–4: Informational Text 6. Determine an author's point of view or purpose in a text and explain how it is conveyed in the text.

Name _____

Read the selection. Then answer the questions that follow.

Imo and the Sweet Potato

Researchers have been studying a colony of macaque monkeys living in Japan on | 13

the island of Koshima since the 1950s. Early on, the scientists began supplying the | 27

monkeys with loads of sweet potatoes, dropping them on the sand near the shoreline. | 41

The potatoes were a big hit, though they were covered with gritty sand. In 1952, an | 57

astonishing thing happened. A young monkey named Imo carried her sweet potato into | 70

the ocean to rinse it before she ate it. Over time, Imo's bright idea changed the behavior | 87

of most members of her colony. Fascinated, the scientists recorded how this big change | 101

took place. | 103

Over the next six years, nearly all of the young monkeys began to wash their | 118

sweet potatoes. Few of the adults (2 out of 11) began to wash theirs. The scientists' | 134

observations led them to conclude that Imo's mother and many of her playmates | 147

learned the behavior from Imo. Male monkeys older than four years, who had little | 161

contact with the younger monkeys, did not learn it. That is, the new behavior traveled | 176

along family lines and through social relationships. By 1959, the young monkeys who | 189

had learned from Imo were adults. They taught their babies the behavior. By January of | 204

1962, nearly all the monkeys of Koshima were wading into the water to rinse sand from | 220

their potatoes. Only mature monkeys born before 1950 did not do so. | 232

Over time, the monkeys came up with other uses for water. Sweet potato washing led | 247

to wheat washing, and then to bathing and swimming for pleasure, and even to utilizing | 262

sea plants and animals for food. Scientists observed such changes with excitement | 274

because they show how culture begins to develop. Imo, by singlehandedly inspiring | 286

change in the Koshima colony's behavior, was a pioneer! | 295

Turn the page.

Answer the questions below.

1 Based on the *first* paragraph, in which of these is the author most interested?

   A the only Koshima macaque monkey with a name

   (B) events in a monkey colony on Koshima Island

   C information about the diet of macaque monkeys

   D reasons why scientists choose to study macaques

2 Which of these word choices *best* shows that the author wants readers to be excited about the subject of this article?

   F sweet; gritty; bright

   G new; younger; pleasure

   (H) astonishing; inspiring

   J mature; singlehandedly

3 From the *last* paragraph, you can tell the author thinks the scientists' conclusions are

   A cultured and well developed.

   (B) accurate and thrilling.

   C changing and still uncertain.

   D unimportant and doubtful.

4 Why do you think the author wrote this article? Explain your answer.

Possible response: The author wanted readers to be engaged by the awesome discovery of how one animal's actions could change the behavior of an entire population.

5 Tell one *difference* between how the potato-washing activity began and how the other water-related behaviors started.

Possible response: Potato-washing got started by one monkey named Imo, who taught the other monkeys. The other water-related behaviors seem to have happened without one monkey teaching the others.

Common Core State Standards

Questions 1–4: Informational Text 6. Determine an author's point of view or purpose in a text and explain how it is conveyed in the text. **Question 5:** Informational Text 1. Cite textual evidence to support analysis of what the text says explicitly as well as inferences drawn from the text.

Read the selection. Then answer the questions that follow.

The Biggest Snowfalls

Imagine your house buried under many feet of snow. Imagine being stuck indoors	13
during a snowstorm that lasted for five or six days. Well, people in the times and places	30
on the chart below experienced just that. These are the greatest snowfalls recorded from	44
the last century up to the year 2000 in the United States. These data were collected by	61
the U.S. Army Corps of Engineers. Do you feel cold just reading the chart, or does it	78
make you wish you could bundle up, go outside, and throw some snowballs?	91
In addition, it's interesting to note, that the lowest temperature on record in the	105
United States, 79.8 degrees below zero Fahrenheit, was observed at Prospect Creek	117
Camp in northern Alaska on January 23, 1971. The lowest in the continental United	131
States was in Rogers Pass, Montana, on January 20, 1954, at –69.7 degrees Fahrenheit.	145
Imagine a record snowfall and record low temperatures almost on the same day!	158

Duration	Place	Date	Inches of Snow
1 month	Tamarack, California	Jan. 1911	390
1 day	Silver Lake, Colorado	Apr. 14–15, 1921	76
1 day	Thompson Pass, Alaska	Dec. 29, 1955	62
1 storm	Mt. Shasta, California	Feb. 13–19, 1959	189
1 storm	Thompson Pass, Alaska	Dec. 26–31, 1955	175
1 season	Mount Baker, Washington	1998–1999	1,140
1 season	Thompson Pass, Alaska	1952–1953	976

Turn the page.

Answer the questions below.

1 This chart would be helpful if you were researching
  A the history of the U.S. Army Corps of Engineers.
  (B) extreme weather in the United States.
  C why snowflakes are each unique.
  D the best sleeping bag for winter camping.

2 The greatest snowfall in a twenty-four-hour period was in
  F Tamarack, California, in 1911.
  G Mt. Shasta, California, in 1959.
  (H) Silver Lake, Colorado, in 1921.
  J Thompson Pass, Alaska, in 1955.

3 The data in this chart lead a reader to conclude that
  A the Army Corps of Engineers monitors all types of weather.
  B more snow falls in the east than in the west.
  C the biggest snowfalls happened in the 1930s.
  (D) Alaska gets more snow than other states.

4 Based on information in the selection and in the chart, what two things can you say about Montana in winter?

Answers may vary. Possible response: Montana appears to get very cold, but does not appear to have any record snowfalls.

Common Core State Standards

Questions 1–4: Informational Text 7. Integrate information presented in different media or formats (e.g., visually, quantitatively) as well as in words to develop a coherent understanding of a topic or issue.

Name _____

Read the selection. Then answer the questions that follow.

Oil: From Under the Ocean to Your Home

The American narrator of *The Cay*, by Theodore Taylor, is a boy named Philip	14
Enright. He lives on a Caribbean island where his father works for the oil industry. A	30
thick dark liquid, oil comes from deep inside the Earth. It is often called "black gold"	46
because it is so valuable to humans. In fact, much of the twentieth century's history	61
can be traced to oil fields around the world and the countries that control them.	76
From the crude oil pumped from underground, people manufacture many modern	87
items, including plastics, tires, ink, and paint. Most importantly, from oil we make all	101
the fuels that power our modern world. Gasoline, kerosene, and diesel and jet fuel are	116
all made from oil. North America has about 15 percent of the world's oil, but we use	133
more oil than the other continents combined. The largest reserves are in Asia, especially	147
the countries of the Middle East, which hold about 75 percent of the world's oil.	162
As you read *The Cay*, you'll learn about this industry in the Carribean in the 1940s	178
and its role in World War Two. You'll understand that drilling for oil was then, and is	195
still today, a highly skilled and often dangerous job involving hundreds of employees	208
and dozens of steps. The chart below shows the process of getting oil from an	223
underground field to a tanker ship, then to a refinery, and finally to a home or school	240
like yours.	242
Is your home or school heated with an oil product? If so, research the cost per gallon	259
this month and how that compares with the price one year ago. Then compare that with	275
the price of oil in 1944, the year in which *The Cay* is set. You'll likely be surprised!	293

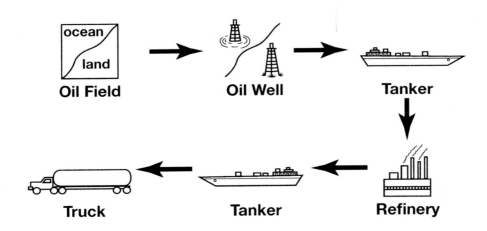

Turn the page.

Answer the questions below.

1 This selection contains a
  A line graph.
  B map.
  Ⓒ flowchart.
  D schedule.

2 The graphic makes it clear that
  Ⓕ tanker ships are part of two stages of oil refining.
  G trucks are the first stage in oil refining.
  H most oil is pumped on land.
  J refineries are the final stage.

3 This selection might best have been used
  Ⓐ to introduce or accompany *The Cay*.
  B as a chapter in *The Cay*.
  C as an article by the main character of *The Cay*.
  D to persuade readers to buy *The Cay*.

4 The graphic about refining suggests that
  F refining oil is an easy task.
  G crude oil refining takes place out in the ocean.
  Ⓗ refining crude oil may pollute the air.
  J oil refineries are small businesses.

5 The content of *The Cay* includes a lot of history and information about the oil industry. Why is the writer's choice of narrator unusual for this type of book?

Answers may vary. Possible response: A young boy would not be expected to know so much about the oil refining industry.

6 Copyright © Pearson Education, Inc., or its affiliates. All Rights Reserved.

Common Core State Standards

Questions 1–5: Informational Text 7. Integrate information presented in different media or formats (e.g., visually, quantitatively) as well as in words to develop a coherent understanding of a topic or issue.

Name _____

Read the selection. Then answer the questions that follow.

A New Kind Of Leadership
by Linda Silver, Staff Reporter

Next year, our school is facing some big changes in its organization. For the past | 15

three years, it was led by a committee of parents and teachers. Beginning next year, a | 31

principal will be hired by the committee to provide leadership and authority while he | 45

works with a cooperative team. The principal will be a new addition to the school, and | 61

most teachers and support staff agree that the time for this kind of change has come. | 77

The chart below shows how this cooperative team will work. The principal will be | 91

chosen and hired by the committee of parents, teachers, and students. Working closely | 104

with the principal will be a team of three people who represent groups of employees | 119

within our school. The chart below shows that in the next year our school will employ | 135

sixteen people to work in new and various roles. | 144

This committee hopes students won't notice much of a difference in the way | 157

things are run, except that they might run more smoothly with only one person in this | 173

leadership role. One person can make a decision more quickly than a whole committee. | 187

Therefore, things might take place more quickly. | 194

Kathy Kovitch, middle grade teacher, says, "It's a very exciting change, and both | 207

students and teachers will be invited to participate in the process of choosing a | 221

principal. It's a chance for us all to think about and discuss what we want in a leader." | 239

Paul Chin, a parent and committee member, says that they hope to make a choice | 254

by June. He also hopes that one or two | 263

students will actively participate in the | 269

search process. He also says that the | 276

committee will continue to exist, but | 282

that it will focus on fundraising and | 289

long-term planning rather than on the | 295

day-to-day running of the school. | 300

Proposal for Cooperative Team

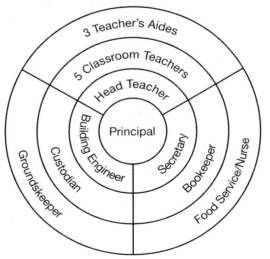

Turn the page.

Answer the questions below.

1 The organizational chart shows that

   A teachers are more important than secretaries.

   B the custodian is not part of the school staff.

   C the staff is disorganized and needs help.

   (D) the principal is the center of the school staff.

2 The chart suggests that

   F teachers must also help with bookkeeping.

   (G) each employee has a specific and clear role.

   H everyone shares all responsibilities.

   J there are too many teachers in this school.

3 Based on the information in the selection, what conclusion can you draw about the school under its new leadership?

   A The school will have more fundraisers under new leadership.

   (B) The school will be managed better under new leadership.

   C The school will have more guest speakers under new leadership.

   D The school will have better attendance under new leadership.

4 Based on the chart and the information in the selection, what three positions will directly work with the principal, and how will that affect the others in the team?

The head teacher, building engineer, and secretary will carry out the decisions made by the principal and will communicate these decisions to the other members of the team.

5 If the chart were a triangle instead of a circle, the principal would be at the top. How would that change what the committee wants the principal to represent?

Answers may vary. Possible responses: A triangle would present the principal as a boss who tells everyone what to do. A circle suggests that the principal is as much a resource as a boss.

Common Core State Standards

Questions 1–5: Informational Text 7. Integrate information presented in different media or formats (e.g., visually, quantitatively) as well as in words to develop a coherent understanding of a topic or issue.

Name _____

Read the selection. Then answer the questions that follow.

January 8

You might not believe me, but my voice is a river, and I'm not kidding. I'm not	17
making up some kind of stupid metaphor. I just know I'm going to be a singer or an	35
actress when I grow up.	40
Most of the time, my voice just flows along, kind of lazy, a little muddy, and no	57
one notices it much, including me. Sometimes after a rain, it gurgles over rocks and	72
splashes with laughter. Sometimes it bends around curves and bubbles over trees	84
that have fallen into it. Sometimes after an angry storm, it roars, all white-capped,	98
dangerous, wild, loud, and ferocious. Sometimes it sings and hums, echoing buzzing	110
insects, cawing crows, or noisy nuthatches. Sometimes it falls suddenly—but it always	123
recovers, pooling up some in the process. Sometimes it is still, quiet, and hardly	137
moving at all. Sometimes it is a mirror. Sometimes it is only breath, just a ripple here	154
and there as blue and green dragonflies alight on its surface.	165

Turn the page.

Answer the questions below.

1 In this selection, the speaker compares her voice with

   A a fallen tree.

   B a metaphor.

   C a dragonfly.

   (D) moving water.

2 The speaker compares laughter to

   F a mirror of the sky.

   (G) a river after rain.

   H an angry storm.

   J buzzing insects.

3 The speaker is most likely

   (A) a young person with dreams.

   B a scientist who studies rivers.

   C a famous singer with a band.

   D a lonely person who watches birds.

4 How do you know that the speaker probably does not think all metaphors are stupid?

The speaker uses metaphors to describe her voice throughout the selection and to present her voice in a positive light.

Common Core State Standards

Questions 1–4: Literature 6. Explain how an author develops the point of view of the narrator or speaker in a text.

Read the selection. Then answer the questions that follow.

Insecurity

It was a cinch, everyone said, nothing to worry about. Miguel's father would put him	15
on a jet in Los Angeles, and his aunt would pick him up in Seattle so he could spend a	35
whole week with his cousins. When his older brother teased him, "You'll never make it	50
past security, shrimp," Miguel tried to ignore the words.	59
The day of his flight, Miguel and his father drove to the airport and hugged	74
good-by, and Miguel entered the line to go through security. After he emptied his	88
pockets, took off his jacket and sneakers, and put them all in the plastic bin, a conveyor	105
belt carried the bin to the X-ray machine. While Miguel waited for a tall, thin man to	122
wave him through the metal detector, his brother's teasing was a mosquito in his ear.	137
As he strolled through, the alarm startled Miguel, and the thin man made him retreat	152
and try again. Again, the alarm sliced the air like a knife, and all the bystanders stopped	169
their conversations and stared. "Over here, please, sir," the thin man waved, frowning,	182
pointing to a bench where a bearded man stood. Miguel watched as a stocky woman	197
waved a wand around the man's forehead and waist.	206
When it was Miguel's turn, he spread his arms and legs like he was in the middle of	224
a jumping jack, and when the wand scanned his chest, it buzzed. "Please empty your	239
pocket, sir," the stocky woman demanded, pointing to Miguel's shirt. Too late, Miguel	252
recalled slipping his professional metal whistle into his shirt pocket, in case his cousins	266
wanted him to referee their soccer game. As he pulled it out, it dangled on its chain.	283
"Nice whistle," she observed, smiling, unlike the thin man. "I'll have to pass it	297
around the X-ray machine."	301
"No problem," Miguel answered, "as long as I can board my plane."	313
"Let's try again," she said, pointing him back to the metal detector. This time,	327
Miguel passed through silently, breathing a deep sigh of relief.	337

Turn the page.

Answer the questions below.

1 The author of this story compared the alarm to
- (**A**) a knife.
- **B** a soccer ball.
- **C** a whistle.
- **D** Miguel's brother.

2 The thin man and the stocky woman were both
- **F** Miguel's friends.
- **G** Miguel's relatives.
- (**H**) security officers.
- **J** television actors.

3 Which phrase does not suggest a comparison in the story?
- **A** like he was in the middle
- (**B**) pointing to a bench
- **C** unlike the thin man
- **D** This time

4 The details of the story suggest that
- **F** Miguel is shy around his cousins.
- **G** Miguel's mother lives in Seattle.
- **H** Miguel flies to Seattle every week.
- (**J**) Miguel has never flown before.

5 Explain the meaning of the metaphor: "His brother's teasing was a mosquito in his ear."

Miguel's brother annoyed him by teasing him. Miguel felt insecure and couldn't seem to get the words out of his head. His brother was like a pesky insect, and the teasing words were the buzzes in his ear.

Common Core State Standards

Questions 1, 5: Literature 6. Explain how an author develops the point of view of the narrator or speaker in a text. **Questions 2–4: Literature 1.** Cite textual evidence to support analysis of what the text says explicitly as well as inferences drawn from the text.

Read the selection. Then answer the questions that follow.

Advertising Proposal

October 13, 2___ | 3

Dear Business Club Members, | 7

As you know, our school store, Lem's Locker, is run by the Business Club as a | 23

nonprofit corporation. Now in its thirteenth year, Lem's sells school supplies, healthy | 35

snacks, and school clothing. Eighty percent of the sales are to students and twenty | 49

percent to their parents. | 53

This year, the staff of Lem's has an advertising budget of $200. These four proposals | 68

are currently on the table: | 73

1. *Place mats in local restaurants.* We can buy a 2" by 4" advertisement printed on | 89
   300,000 paper place mats that will be distributed among four popular restaurants: | 101
   The Great Wall, Boomers Café, Millie's Diner, and South of the Border. The | 114
   printer says it takes about one year for the restaurants to go through this many | 129
   place mats. Twenty ads form a border, printed in red or green on white. Cost: $200. | 145

2. *Advertisements in local movie theaters.* We could use the school's video studio to | 158
   produce a thirty-second commercial. Cost to produce: $50. Cost to run: $100 per | 171
   month. The theater advertisement agency estimates seven hundred people would | 181
   see our ad per week and that over half of these are students. | 194

3. *Signs at the town playing fields.* These professionally painted metal signs are | 206
   guaranteed for fifty years. Cost: $140 each. | 213

4. *Postcards with discount coupons.* Mailing a postcard to every household in our | 225
   school would give people something to hang on their refrigerators. In-house | 236
   printing cost for six hundred cards: $60; Postage: $180. | 245

We should continue to brainstorm new ideas. I propose that we vote on these | 259

proposals at the next meeting, November 14 at 3 P.M. in the auditorium. I hope to see | 276

you there. Until then, support our school store whenever you can by making purchases | 290

and volunteering to work. Thank you. | 296

Yours in business, | 299

Tamara Douglass, President | 302

Turn the page.

Answer the questions below.

1 **Which form of advertising is the least expensive?**
(A) place mats in local restaurants
B three months of movie theater ads
C three signs at the town fields
D printing and mailing six hundred postcards

2 **Which form of advertising would last the longest?**
F place mats
G movie theater ads
(H) signs at playing fields
J postcards with coupons

3 **Which sentence expresses a contrast?**
A Both the postcards and the place mats could use the same design.
B The place mats and the postcards appeal to parents.
C I think the movie theater ads cost too much.
(D) The signs are outdoors, but the place mats are indoors.

4 **Based on the Business Club's budget, how many of the proposals can they act on? Explain your answer.**

They can only act on one proposal because acting on more than one would cost more than they have budgeted.

5 **If the Business Club wishes to increase the percentage of sales to parents, which two proposals seem most promising?**

Postcards and place mats seem most likely to be seen by parents.

Common Core State Standards

Questions 1–5: **Informational Text 1.** Cite textual evidence to support analysis of what the text says explicitly as well as inferences drawn from the text.

Name _____

Read the selection. Then answer the questions that follow.

Stool Pigeons

Have you ever heard of someone being called a "stool pigeon"? This phrase refers	14
to someone who tattles or reports on someone else's wrongdoings. If one of a team of	30
bank robbers goes to the police to tell on all of them, the rest of the team of robbers	49
might consider that person a "rat." If the rat participated in the robbery in order to get	66
evidence and report it, that person is a stool pigeon.	76
Where did this figure of speech come from? In the 1700s, North American hunters	90
searched for pigeons as targets. First, they caught one live bird and tied it to a stump	107
that looked like a seat or stool. As the bird flapped its wings, it would attract other	124
pigeons, giving the hunters more targets. The live bird was a trick. Later, in the	139
language of the 1800s, a "stool pigeon" or "stoolie" began to refer to someone who	154
lured lawbreakers into his or her trust, and then reported them to the law.	168

Turn the page.

Answer the questions below.

1 In this selection, the author

    A informs readers about pigeons.

    B persuades readers to try hunting.

    (C) explains a figure of speech.

    D wishes to become a stool pigeon.

2 The author of this passage is most likely someone who

    F works in law enforcement.

    (G) likes knowing the origins of words.

    H teaches college English.

    J has broken the law.

3 This selection suggests that figures of speech

    A only last a few years.

    (B) can be hundreds of years old.

    C are always about birds.

    D don't make much logical sense.

4 What do the terms "dog-eared" and "hog wild" appear to have in common with the term "stool pigeon"?

All the terms refer to animal behavior and have come to have a new meaning.

Common Core State Standards

Questions 1–3: Informational Text 6. Determine an author's point of view or purpose in a text and explain how it is conveyed in the text. **Question 4: Informational Text 1.** Cite textual evidence to support analysis of what the text says explicitly as well as inferences drawn from the text.

Name _____

Read the selection. Then answer the questions that follow.

The Case of the Missing Calculator

Mr. Feeny has taught math at Cook County Middle School for over twenty years. He	15
loves his students, his textbooks, his classroom, and his computer. He loves the posters	29
on his walls and the windows that overlook the soccer fields behind the school. But	44
most of all, he loves his new calculators.	52
Last summer, Mr. Feeny convinced the Math Department to purchase twenty	63
QV-160s, the most powerful student calculators on the market. They came in a locked	77
suitcase designed to hold a class set. Each calculator was numbered in permanent white	91
ink, from one to twenty. At the beginning of every class, Mr. Feeny unlocks the suitcase	107
and distributes the calculators. He does this six times a day, with six different groups of	123
students. At the end of every class, he checks to make sure they are all in order in their	142
cozy little slots. At the end of every class, they are always accounted for.	156
Except for today: calculator #14 is missing. Mr. Feeny searches the classroom, but	169
it's not here. He opens his six desk drawers, but there is no calculator. He looks through	186
the bookcase—no calculator. He begins to think about his last class, focusing on his	201
movements.	202
Mr. Feeney remembers handing out the calculators to his class. He had walked	215
around the classroom using his own QV-160 to check students' work. He had left the	230
room for a moment to speak with another teacher, Mrs. Patel.	241
Later, he asked her whether she had seen anything that might explain what had	255
happened. As he told his story, she began to smile. "Are you sure you didn't switch	271
your own calculator with #14?" she asked. "My own is right here," Mr. Feeny said, and	287
removed it from his right hand coat pocket. "And in your other pocket?" she asked.	302
There, in the pocket, is #14.	308

Turn the page.

Answer the questions below.

1 The author of this story means to

A express that students are untrustworthy.

B explain why expensive equipment should be locked up.

C persuade readers to buy a QV-160.

(D) entertain readers with a surprise ending.

2 The story makes it clear that Mr. Feeny

(F) placed #14 in his own pocket.

G cannot trust all his students.

H should no longer be teaching math.

J should buy more than twenty calculators.

3 The details in the second paragraph lead us to conclude that

A the QV-160 is overrated.

B only a few students use the QV-160s.

C many calculators have been stolen from the school.

(D) Mr. Feeny is very careful with the calculators.

4 The last sentence suggests that

F Mr. Feeny would never find the missing calculator.

G a student probably took the calculator.

H the students hadn't left for the day.

(J) Mr. Feeny will feel foolish.

5 The teacher might have learned a lesson in this story. What lesson about drawing conclusions does "The Case of the Missing Calculator" illustrate?

The lesson the story teaches is that anyone can make a mistake, and that others can help us solve problems.

Common Core State Standards

Question 1: Informational Text 6. Determine an author's point of view or purpose in a text and explain how it is conveyed in the text. **Questions 2–4: Informational Text 3.** Analyze in detail how a key individual, event, or idea is introduced, illustrated, and elaborated in a text (e.g., through examples or anecdotes). **Question 5: Informational Text 2.** Determine a central idea of a text and how it is conveyed through particular details; provide a summary of the text distinct from personal opinions or judgments.

Name _____

Read the selection. Then answer the questions that follow.

No More Dragons

Back in the days when everything was new, there existed a dragon, a gigantic flying | 15

creature with green scales, wide wings, and a long, powerful tail. Dragon was surely | 29

handsome and strong, but he was also a bully who teased the other animals. Dragon | 44

often picked arguments, especially with creatures smaller than himself, and, of course, | 56

he always won. He even gobbled fireflies when he wasn't all that hungry. The other | 71

animals begged him to stop, but Dragon would not heed their warnings. "He's very | 85

scary," observed Skunk. "And very dangerous," accused Deer. | 93

One summer, Dragon ate so many fireflies, he began to breathe flames. Whenever he | 107

felt aggressive, he could shoot fire at any target he chose. "You've got to be careful!" | 123

the animals cried. "When the Creator sees what you have done, you will be in trouble!" | 139

But Dragon didn't listen; he laughed. | 145

One September night while Dragon slept, he snored and the entire forest burst into | 159

flames! As oak trees burned into black spikes, Eagle and Owl flew many kilometers | 173

away, and Trout and Pike took refuge on the river bottom. The empty forest reeked of | 189

smoke, and countless animals lost their homes. For this, the Creator punished Dragon | 202

with the following decree: "From this day forward, Dragon, you will no longer be | 216

gigantic and strong, but tiny and weak. You will not soar among the clouds, but buzz | 232

along the river's surface, as low as a creature can fly. Your wings will no longer be | 249

thick and muscular, but paper-thin and delicate. Your body will not be powerful and | 263

green, but slender and black, and from now on, your name will be *dragonfly*." | 277

So if you spot a dragonfly flitting across the surface of a pond, recall Dragon and | 293

his arrogant mistake. Be gentle with the forest and your friends, or a similar fate could | 309

befall you. | 311

Turn the page.

Answer the questions below.

1 You can tell from the first paragraph that you are reading

   A a newspaper article.

   B a letter.

   C an autobiography.

   (D) a legend.

2 When Dragon laughed at the end of the second paragraph, it means that

   (F) he didn't care what the others said.

   G his throat was tickled by the fireflies.

   H he thought the Creator was very funny.

   J he thought everyone was joking.

3 The Creator in this story appears to be a

   A bird.

   (B) judge.

   C dragon.

   D bully.

4 In the last paragraph, the author explicitly writes about the story's lesson or moral. Do you think the author exaggerates here or means what he or she says literally?

Answers may vary. Possible response: I think the author exaggerates here because I do not believe I might be turned into an insect.

5 After reading this story, one student concluded, "This punishment is too harsh. The Creator could have taught Dragon a lesson without. . . ." Identify what aspect of the Creator's lesson might have seemed too harsh and explain how the punishment could have been milder.

Answers may vary. Possible response: The Creator could have punished the Dragon without changing him so dramatically. The Creator could have made him smaller but not incredibly small, or just taken away his fire-breathing ability.

Common Core State Standards

Questions 1–3: Literature 1. Cite textual evidence to support analysis of what the text says explicitly as well as inferences drawn from the text.
Questions 4, 5: Literature 2. Determine a theme or central idea of a text and how it is conveyed through particular details; provide a summary of the text distinct from personal opinions or judgments.

Read the selection. Then answer the questions that follow.

What Do Teenagers Eat?

To find out what teenagers at our middle school eat, I took a survey of one hundred | 17

of our students, ages twelve to fifteen, during the week of April 14. I asked them to rate | 35

how often they eat certain kinds of foods. A chart showing the raw data is shown below. | 52

When asked how often they eat fresh fruits, vegetables, and salads, 17 percent | 65

replied "never." About two-thirds of us eat these sometimes and only 20 percent of us | 80

eat them daily. | 83

Every one of us eats pizza and chips. They are the universal teenage foods. A dozen | 99

of us admit to eating pizza every day! | 107

There were a few surprises. For example, three out of every four students drink | 121

bottled water every day. Also, over a third of us eat candy every day. Only 15 percent of | 139

us don't eat meat, and a third of us never eat fish. Over half of us drink soda every day. | 159

You can draw your own conclusions, but I think this survey shows that most students | 174

at Middleton Middle School need to improve their diets! | 183

	Never	Sometimes	Daily
Fresh fruit, vegetables, salad	17	63	20
Cereal	32	51	17
Chips	0	79	21
Pizza	0	88	12
Candy	3	58	39
Chicken or beef	15	70	15
Fish	33	62	5
Sugary desserts	2	53	45
Soda	3	37	60
Bottled water	1	24	75
Milk	24	44	32

Turn the page.

Answer the questions below.

1 The students at this school
- **(A)** eat more pizza than salad.
- **B** eat fish every day.
- **C** never eat sugary desserts.
- **D** drink more milk than bottled water.

2 Which of these is a valid generalization?
- **F** Most students never drink milk.
- **(G)** Most students eat fruits or vegetables sometimes.
- **H** Many middle school students don't eat meat.
- **J** Cereal is a popular breakfast among middle school students.

3 Which of these is an invalid generalization about the teenagers surveyed?
- **A** Everyone eats pizza and chips.
- **(B)** All students occasionally eat sugary desserts.
- **C** Nearly everyone drinks bottled water.
- **D** More vegetarians eat pizza than eat chips.

4 What, after pizza and chips, appears to be a nearly "universal" teenage favorite? Explain your answer.

Soda appears to be a nearly universal teenage favorite. Over half the teenagers surveyed drink it every day.

Common Core State Standards

Questions 1–4: Informational Text 7. Integrate information presented in different media or formats (e.g., visually, quantitatively) as well as in words to develop a coherent understanding of a topic or issue.

Name _____

Read the selection. Then answer the questions that follow.

Chapter Two

My mom and dad were married at the town landfill, and yes, I am certain of this | 17
because I've seen the photographs. Dad ran the Transfer Station (as they called it | 31
officially) in Bethel, Ohio, and Mom took a part-time job there on Saturdays and | 45
Sundays. Well, Dad started showing up on Saturdays and Sundays even though he | 58
wasn't scheduled, and the next thing you know they were having dinner on Saturday | 72
evenings and again on Sundays. After a year, they decided that the Transfer Station | 86
would run a lot more smoothly if they returned to their regular hours, which meant that | 102
they ought to get married so they wouldn't have to rely on the landfill to see each other. | 120

So when it came time to organize the wedding, the landfill seemed the logical site. | 135
They spread carpets all around and built a fancy wooden canopy in the unloading zone. | 150
Some three hundred wedding guests cheered as the limousine pulled up to the recycling | 164
bins and they tiptoed out, Dad in a tuxedo and top hat and Mom in a full-length, white | 182
wedding gown. Someone spread rose petals in front of my mother as she walked to the | 198
canopy where the town clerk waited. As the happy couple recited vows of everlasting | 212
love, several of my dad's friends attached the longest, loudest chain of clatter behind | 226
the limousine with a sign that said "Just Married: Don't 'Dump' Me Yet!" As they | 241
drove away to the inn for the reception, my mother's brother Jared sang a tune he'd | 257
written especially for the occasion called "Recycled Love." | 265

"Sure, it was a funny place for a wedding," my mother recalls today, "but it was also | 282
unique. Our marriage was one of a kind . . . right from the start." I swear I laugh every | 302
time I stare at those photographs. | 308

Turn the page.

Answer the questions below.

1 What did the writer's parents have in common as the story begins?

A love of roses

(B) working at the Transfer Station

C wanting to get married

D desire to ride in a limousine

2 The story shows that the speaker's parents were

(F) willing to do something unusual.

G extremely traditional.

H sentimental about how they met.

J unhappy with their jobs.

3 Which of the following features of the speaker's parents' wedding is probably not typical of most weddings?

A the canopy

B the attire

(C) the setting

D the photos

4 The "voice" of this memoir is

(F) casual and friendly, like a story with a voice.

G formal to the point of being stuffy.

H written like a newspaper article.

J very emotional because of the content.

5 Does the speaker find his or her parents' wedding photos more amusing or embarrassing? Explain your answer.

The author finds his or her parents' wedding more amusing than embarrassing because he or she laughs whenever he or she looks at the pictures and seems to have looked at them and asked about them more than a few times.

Common Core State Standards

Questions 1–3: Informational Text 1. Cite textual evidence to support analysis of what the text says explicitly as well as inferences drawn from the text.
Questions 4, 5: Informational Text 6. Determine an author's point of view or purpose in a text and explain how it is conveyed in the text.

178

Fresh Reads   Unit 6 Week 5 OL

Name _____

Read the selection. Then answer the questions that follow.

The Sea Lamprey: A Nervous System Model

The sea lamprey is a fascinating animal that lives in water. It is born in rivers	16
that flow to the sea in many parts of northeastern North America. At the end of its	33
"adolescence," the lamprey transforms into an adult and heads to the ocean to live out	48
its adult life.	51
Lampreys look like eels. Unlike eels, they have no bones, though their bodies do	65
contain a spinal cord. Lampreys spend their first seven years burrowed in the sand in	80
freshwater streams. Blind during this stage of life, they feed on nutrients in the water	95
and breathe through gills. At the time of their transformation, lampreys grow eyes and	109
sucker mouths, and their limber bodies turn from brown to black and silver. They also	124
grow from six to twelve inches to as much as three feet after they complete their adult	141
journey out to sea.	145
Biologists, especially the ones who study how nerves function during injury and	157
healing, are interested in lampreys. Some of these biologists discovered that if you cut	171
a young lamprey's spinal cord, the nerves will grow back together again. The healed	185
animal can swim just as well as it did before its spinal cord was cut! Curious to know	203
more about this amazing ability, biologists catch lampreys and use them to study nerve	217
regeneration, the ability of a nerve to grow back after it has been cut.	231
Thanks to the secrets this unusual creature offers and the scientists who study them,	245
nerve damage in human spinal cords may one day be able to be repaired.	259

Turn the page.

Answer the questions below.

1 How do adult lampreys differ from young ones?

   A They have a spinal cord.

   B They live in fresh water.

   C They are brown.

   (D) They have eyes.

2 Which of these is a valid generalization?

   F Some biologists spend seven years studying one stream.

   G When the human spinal cord is cut, it grows back.

   (H) When animals transform, they change physically.

   J Most scientists who study lampreys also study eels.

3 Which of these is a faulty generalization?

   A Lampreys may shed light on nerve regeneration.

   B Underwater, eels are often mistaken for lampreys.

   C Vertebrates are animals with backbones.

   (D) All eels lack a spinal cord but have bones.

4 Is the following generalization valid or faulty? Give your reasons.

A cure for most types of human spinal cord injury will come from the study of lampreys.

This is a faulty generalization. Even if scientists can discover how and why the lamprey's spinal cord heals itself and apply that to cure human injuries, it is unclear whether such a cure will work for "most" types of human spinal cord injuries.

5 When the lamprey transforms, two of its general needs must change; otherwise it would not leave the river or stream or grow so much in length. Generalize from those two details what two basic needs of the lamprey must change as a result of its transformation.

As a result of its transformation, the lamprey needs a saltwater environment and food that is not available or not available in sufficient quantity in the freshwater environment.

Common Core State Standards

Questions 1–5: Informational Text 1. Cite textual evidence to support analysis of what the text says explicitly as well as inferences drawn from the text. **Informational Text 3.** Analyze in detail how a key individual, event, or idea is introduced, illustrated, and elaborated in a text (e.g., through examples or anecdotes).